LETHAL LEGACY

BSE – the search for the truth

Dr Stephen Dealler

MBChB, DCM, DTMH, FRSTMH, MRC Path, MD

BLOOMSBURY

This edition first published in 1996 by
Bloomsbury Publishing Plc
2 Soho Square
London, W1V 6HB

A copy of the CIP entry for this book is
available from the British Library

ISBN 0 7475 2904 3

Design by AB3
Typeset by Hewer Text Composition Services, Edinburgh
Printed and bound in Great Britain by
Cox & Wyman Ltd, Reading, Berks

To everyone who has kept me going over the past few years. To be the messenger with bad news takes more guts than I had on my own.

Contents

Acknowledgements

Information for this book came from all the sources of the scientific world. To mention them all would be impossible here. The major scientists and their departments throughout the world provided me with the details that they realised were important. They also knew that the economic pressure on scientific funding and the UK regulations on the release of data did not allow them to let these data out directly. I would particularly like to thank Helen Grant and James Erlichman, who have stood behind me all the way; and Professor Roy Postlethwaite, Ann Maddocks and Martin Schweiger, who through their knowledge and determination have helped to set up the Spongiform Encephalopathy Research Campaign, now a registered charity.

The information contained in this book reflects my own opinions, which are not necessarily those of the publishers.

Every care has been taken to ensure the accuracy of the information contained in this publication, to the best of my ability at the time of publication. However, knowledge about BSE is constantly changing, and to ensure that future editions of this book are kept up to date, readers are invited to write to me c/o Bloomsbury Publishing Plc, 2 Soho Square, London W1V 6HB.

Introduction

This book is an account of the growth of information about BSE, which started as a few cases on a single farm and has become potentially one of the major causes of human death. I have largely told it as a personal story: for several years I have worked my way through the information on the subject and then fought to get the worrying data through to those people in the UK who were responsible for making the decisions. All the way I had been told that this approach would not work, and that the only way to get anything done was through the media. The making of a *World in Action* programme in 1995 eventually got the news through to the public. It showed that we were eating large numbers of infected cattle . . . including parts that were specifically considered to be infective.

BSE is just one of a list of similar diseases that are known in animals. All we could say about it when it arrived was what we knew about the others: fatal, untreatable, passed on by eating the tissue of an infected animal, found in all the tissues of the body (but in some much more than others), and not destroyed by domestic cooking. BSE would have a huge incubation period (a large proportion of the life expectancy of the animal) and would kill around 50% of the animals exposed to enough of it. Clearly this was not something like flu, which would kill 0.01%, but bad enough to cause a major epidemic at immense cost over the following 50 years.

I have tried to avoid the political side of why misinformation was given to the public, why misleading data was released to the press, why a risk was considered acceptable even though the level of risk was unknown. My story is just that of a messenger who has had to deal with the pressures of all sides and has had to explain what is happening in terms of the listener.

The problem that we are left with, after 10 years of a bovine epidemic, can currently hardly be quantified. What about our farmers? After all, they have done nothing wrong and are paying for errors made by the Government in the early 1980s. What about the population? After all, we (and that includes me) have been eating potentially infective material since the early 1980s. At the moment we are standing and waiting to see if more people die. I think the book puts it plainly that, although compensation will help in the meantime, it is scientific research that will get us out, not finger-crossing.

This book is for a wide audience – shoppers, parents, farmers, members of the scientific community and many others. We all need to know. Inevitably some of the arguments have to be supported by complex data. If you find that off-putting, ignore it and read on. There is enough information here of different kinds for everyone to see the picture.

CHAPTER ONE

BSE: a growing awareness

Every Monday at 12 noon the medical microbiologists of Leeds General Infirmary held a meeting. We would discuss the cases that had come in during the previous weekend and pass on any information necessary. Six of us were there on this particular Monday in June 1988, all highly qualified and cosily crammed into one small corner of the laboratory in the Old Medical School. The discussion turned to listeriosis, which was making headlines at the time.

'Well, if you think that's a killer,' said Kevin, 'have a look at bovine spongiform encephalopathy. Did anyone else see the article in the *BMJ*?'

'Definitely not a disease to be recommended,' added Paul. 'In fact, if they're right, it's the sort of thing to wipe out whole populations, never mind a few pregnant women.'

At this time, I have to confess, I hadn't even heard of the disease, let alone read the article in the *British Medical Journal*. Being due to take a Royal College of Pathologists' examination in a few months' time, I decided that this was yet another subject that I had to find out about. I could just imagine myself being interrogated by a pair of stern-faced senior pathologists on diseases I hadn't read up on.

The University of Leeds has an excellent and well-equipped medical library, and that afternoon I decided to make full use of it to do a rapid search for information

3

about BSE. The library has a CD-ROM computer search and retrieval system, which is now in common use but which was then something of a novelty. To get CD-ROM to search, it needs to be given a word or subject which it can compare with all the data in its memory and pick out any article mentioning that word or subject. I sat down and typed 'Bovine spongiform encephalopathy' into the keyboard, answered a few questions that came up on the screen and then waited for the titles of the publications to arrive, each with a short abstract of what the paper was about. On most subjects I had previously looked up in this way I would be told that there were over a hundred references. This time, however, there was almost no data at all: a single article in the *Veterinary Record*, a few minor pieces and one in the *BMJ*.

T.A. Holt, a senior house officer from St James's Hospital, London, and J. Phillips, a dietician, were the first from the medical profession to read about BSE and realise that this was no ordinary bug. It was one of a group of diseases that were fatal, could not be destroyed by cooking, could not be treated and were passed from one species to another. They described the handling of BSE up to that time, one of slaughter and incineration of animals with clinical disease, as naive, uninformed and potentially disastrous. They made it quite clear that, although brain was 'prohibited offal' and hence could not be included in uncooked food such as sausages, it could be included in cooked offal quite easily. It could even be called 'meat', as indeed that was what it was. Canteen food could easily contain it. They pointed out that since we could not know which animals were infected and which were not at the time of sale it would be better, if not to ban British beef brain, at least to warn the population of its presence in food. They were also unhappy that the maximum penalty for breaking the law by including brain in certain foods was only £1000 (even in 1996 the fine is only £5000). And who was going to find out anyway? *British Medical Journal*, June 1988.

This, in the world of medical research, was a little peculiar. Researchers on the whole tend to be wary of making statements which they can't support. So why was this writer, Dr Holt, saying in the *BMJ* that everyone in the UK was at risk, when there was so little data to work from? His claim was that bovine tissue in human food derived from BSE-infected cattle represented a risk to those who were eating it. My curiosity was aroused; it was the beginning of a long, difficult and frustrating search for the truth.

It turned out that in fact there was enough data at that time to draw the conclusions to which he had come. The reason that there was so little available for my purposes was that BSE was very new, and there had simply been too little time for it to have reached the medical and veterinary journals. This was exacerbated by the fact that most of the information had come from MAFF (the Ministry of Agriculture, Fisheries and Food) veterinary sources, and MAFF is not known for publishing its information in scientific journals.

Spongiform encephalopathy (SE) is the name given to a specific disease because of the appearance under the microscope of the brain of an infected animal. The build-up of damage to the nervous tissue leads to the gradual death of the major brain cells, and the resultant holes look like the holes in a sponge. It was only found very late that this type of disease was actually transmissible from one animal to another by the inoculation of tissue. A long incubation period and certain death follow.

Small beginnings

The recorded origins of BSE were as follows: in November 1986, a farmer in the south of England had noticed problems in a number of the cattle in his milking herd. They started to behave strangely, be afraid of him, act abnormally when milked. After a few weeks of such changes in temperament,

5

physical symptoms started to set in. The skin would shake and tremble at times due to muscular effects underneath, the cow would start to stagger and eventually could not stand up. It would lose its appetite and its milk yield would go down. Worried about the affected cows and the possible effects on the rest of his herd, the farmer called in the vet. Various attempts at treatment had only short-term effects; the animals inevitably died. I am now told that he had six such cases on his farm.

The brains of the animals were removed and sent to the neuropathologist at the Central Veterinary Laboratory (CVL) in Weybridge, south-west of London. Under the microscope it was clear that the brains showed damage in the form of a spongiform encephalopathy; the changes in the brain were similar to those found in scrapie, a known disease of sheep. The farmer, concerned that more of his herd might go (as indeed they did), thought that if nothing else he should publicise his misfortune as a scientific 'find' of interest to the rest of the farming community. This was, after all, the first scientific report of BSE in the world. What actually happened was that he did not publish anything at all. The cattle that showed the signs of the disease were slaughtered and possibly buried by direction of MAFF. The farmer may have been asked not to make public his information about the findings, nor to send the data to any scientific journals.

K.L. Morgan from Bristol asked why this type of disease should turn up in cattle just now. Maybe it was because there were more sheep (16% more since 1981, and even greater increases in lowland areas) and more with scrapie (no data recorded, and dead sheep were often just buried). He decided that BSE's wide appearance all over the UK could not be due to such a fact: surely it must be due to some infective agent being delivered to the farm. How about the meat and bone meal in protein supplements, which makes up 5% of dairy rations? It was actually made from inedible sheep offal and seemed a viable hypothesis. The change in the rendering process, with the removal of the system that used acetone, or other organic solvent, to remove the fatty material, and the lowering of the temperatures at which this process was carried out, took place at the beginning of the 1980s. Perhaps that was what had led to scrapie being fed to cattle? He felt that high temperatures (140°C) should be reintroduced and that the Government should stop any shortsightedness in the approach to nationwide control of scrapie. 'BSE: time to take scrapie seriously', editorial in the *Veterinary Record*, 30 April 1988.

After all the meat has been removed from a carcass at the slaughterhouse, renderers extract the remaining proteinaceous materials and fats for industrial purposes. These products are used, for instance, in animal feed, lipsticks, some margarines and many processed foods.

Two of the reasons that the change in rendering regulations took place were to use less energy and to reduce the risk to abattoir workers. This may have turned out to be a very short-term view.

The Bovine Spongiform Encephalopathy (Amendment) Order 1988 Statutory Instrument 1345 and 1346

Compensation was introduced on 8 August 1988 to pay farmers for cattle considered to suffer from BSE. This was to be 50% of the value of the cow and was to be agreed between the MAFF VO (veterinary officer) and the farmer at the time of his visit. BSE cattle were automatically the property of MAFF and would be destroyed. The farmer must release them, and anyone who had taken tissue from a cow that was subsequently found to have BSE would be obliged to release it to MAFF if it was demanded.

By 1987 it was quite clear that BSE was not going to go away. All over the UK, other farmers were reporting similar cases and it was getting worse. Not only were the cases appearing in a widespread pattern but the numbers were rising fast. It was decided – by whom is unknown – that the details of the first case should be published so that science could at last do some hard and fast research into what was happening.

MAFF officials did not know it then, but they were already too late to stop one of the biggest epidemics of disease British agriculture had ever seen. Based on current calculations, around 350,000 cattle would develop the symptoms of BSE by the end of the epidemic, and in the same period (up to the year 2000) we will have eaten 1,800,000 infected cattle; that is to say, cattle that would have died of BSE before the age of 10 had we not eaten them first. Potentially, this was the greatest risk to Britain's human population since the Black Death; but it took five years of research for me to discover that, and by then it was already too late to prevent the risk.

TSEs: BSE and its relatives

I was distinctly disappointed by the amount of information which had been released by 1988. I could only assume that MAFF quite simply did not have the data to make public and that all their decisions on how to handle BSE would therefore have to be made in the light of the results from the previous 30 years of intensive research into other spongiform encephalopathies in animals.

What had started as an exercise in hedging my bets for the pathology exam was turning into a maze of unknown paths and blind alleys. Although no one could attach any blame to me for knowing no more on the subject than had been published, I couldn't let things rest. The only way forward was to read up on all the other known transmissible spongiform encephalopathies (TSEs) to see if they would give me some insight into BSE. Weighty textbooks were available on the subject of Creutzfeldt-Jakob disease (the main TSE of humans) and there were wads of literature on scrapie. However, the one thing that quickly became clear was that the same names appeared over and over again on the vast majority of texts. I also noticed that the works were written in a specific way, as if the reader was expected to understand many terms that were not common even in scientific circles. These scientists were relatively small groups of researchers spread about the world, and they appeared to be writing mainly for each other, to announce or refute theories or research. The articles they were producing often contained little that was new; the views they were expressing had been expressed elsewhere. Every now and then an exciting find would appear and would be chased determinedly with heavyweight research. However, my over-riding impression was that only a few people in the world understood the subject of TSEs, and even they disagreed amongst themselves. If this was so, how were the UK Government to get coherent advice on the problem of BSE?

The Creutzfeldt-Jakob aisease (CJD) that we have been seeing in the UK for many years has been highly variable, with initial symptoms appearing in people over 50 years of age and being anything from a decreasing ability to speak properly, or merely tripping or dropping things. These symptoms slowly progress during the degeneration of the brain to produce the loss of complex functions of the brain (speech, memory, understanding) and basic functions (movement, balance, breathing). The disease generally causes death within six months, but slowly progressing cases of up to 10 years have been reported. The cases seen after 1993 in younger people (less than 42 years of age) progress relatively slowly, with physical symptoms appearing early and death taking place after two years. These are the cases felt to be derived from BSE.

Richard Race in Montana shows that scrapie can be grown in brain cancer cells in test tubes but that only a small amount of infection was present in each cell. No damage could be seen in the cells themselves, and scrapie infection from a species that was not the same as the species from which the tumour came could not be infected at all. *Journal of General Virology*, 1987.

The group of diseases found in animals and man known as transmissible spongiform encephalopathies all show the same appearance through the microscope: an affected animal has holes in its brain tissue (hence 'spongiform') and a decrease in the amount of nervous tissue. They are transmissible in that they can be transferred from one animal to another via the food chain (known as inoculation by mouth). This feature separates them from other diseases which exhibit spongiform changes. TSEs appear to be divided into those diseases which appear naturally and those which can be produced in animals as a result of human error or experimentation. When I started looking into this area in 1988 the known natural diseases in humans were Creutzfeldt-Jakob disease (CJD), kuru (a TSE associated with cannibalism in New Guinea) and the Gerstmann-Straussler-Scheinker (GSS) syndrome. In animals, they were scrapie in sheep and goats, transmissible mink encephalopathy (TME) and chronic wasting disease of deer (CWDD). These diseases had been transmitted both experimentally and accidentally to many other species, but there was no recognised natural disease of cattle.

Gajdusek from Washington reviewed what had happened to the people in New Guinea, the Fore tribe, that permitted cannibalism of dead members. Just after the Second World War and possibly earlier there was an outbreak of a new disease, kuru, in which people, particularly women and children, would develop a spongiform encephalopathy. Most of the patients were under the age of 25, but some were still appearing in the 1980s long after the ban on cannibalism in 1957. This showed that the incubation period of the disease could be very long and presumably depended on the dose of disease that was eaten. *Virology*, 1990.

In 1920 and 1921 two scientists, Jakob and Creutzfeldt, had independently discovered a human disease in which patients not only became demented, but also lost their physical as well as complex mental abilities, relatively early in their lifespan. We are used to people losing much of their brainpower when they are very old, and indeed it is quite easy to think of it as normal degeneration of the brain; but in younger people, often between the ages of forty and sixty, this appears strange and is seen as a disease rather than as a natural progression. The number of cases of CJD had not been properly studied until after the Second World War; when it was, cases seemed to be relatively steady throughout the world wherever measured, and to occur at a similar rate almost everywhere. It seemed to affect about one person per million of the population per annum. In a small number of places, however, it appeared to be dramatically more frequent than elsewhere; the reason was then still unclear. Another strange factor was that 5–15% of cases seemed to be in families that had already experienced the disease; however, the parents of an affected person might never show any sign. In other words, although it could be transmitted in families some members might carry the trait and pass it on but show no symptoms themselves.

Paul Brown from Washington investigated the numbers of cases of CJD in France. Between 1968 and 1982 there had been 329 cases. CJD was most likely to appear in a patient between the ages of 50 and 74 with an average of 60.8 yrs. There were slightly more women than men dying, and 6% of cases were associated with others in the same family. There was an excess of cases in the Paris area and in other large cities but otherwise there was no obvious cluster of cases in the country. He could find no particular association between occupation or birthplace with the disease. There was an odd finding that people who married into families affected by CJD occasionally developed the disease, as had been found in other countries. *Neurology*, June 1987.

Mr Thompson, the Parliamentary Secretary to the Ministry of Agriculture announced the total amounts of exports (tonnes) managed by the rendering industry, but admitted that meat and bone meal were only part of the figures and not kept as separate statistics.

	1986	1987	1988
Flours, meals, pellets of meat or offal unfit for human consumption	10,001	12,299	13,228
Bone meal	3,902	5,061	5,174

At the time many people were wondering where this was going and what was it going to produce in terms of disease abroad. Meat and bone meal must have been in food for 40 years, and certainly the customers must have been like us in not expecting a toxin in the feed.

Scrapie is a disease of sheep (principally) and goats, found predominantly in the merino sheep of western Europe, and has been known about for centuries. These sheep were derived from a group in northern Spain that had particularly soft wool and were considered so valuable that the kings of Spain would reward their allies by gifts of small flocks. Although this was not the only way in which they spread around Europe, it provides some explanation of why scrapie only became known in Britain from the mid-eighteenth century, perhaps carried genetically by the merino.

I found scrapie a fascinating disease and the familial factors involved in it were clear. Since the merino sheep were interbred with other strains and the resulting animals severely inbred to produce genetically reliable strains of animal (which could then be sold for a high price), it was clear that susceptibility to scrapie was not considered the most important trait to eliminate. It did actually seem possible to breed sheep so that they were more and more or less and less likely to suffer from scrapie. In fact it seemed almost (but not quite) possible to breed the disease out of a flock – in other words, the tendency could be reduced but not eliminated. So, since sheep that suffer from scrapie have dramatically fewer offspring than those that don't, why had this scrapie-prone familial trait not been bred out of the flocks long ago? At this point in my reading I supposed that it was because of the inbreeding and the retention of certain flock characteristics for breed purposes. This is, however a very strange characteristic: an apparently genetic trait that cannot be bred out of an inbred group. All that appeared possible with breeding programmes was to decrease the chances of an animal developing the disease.

The expansion of British wool production for the cloth mills of the eighteenth and nineteenth centuries made sheep breeding a major industry and was followed by the export of pure-bred stocks to the Empire. Where the sheep went, so did the disease – except to Australia and New Zealand, where infected flocks did not seem to pass the disease on to their offspring. This seemed exceptionally curious to me. The logical conclusion was that there was an environmental factor required to permit the disease to be passed on to the offspring. British sheep exported to Iceland also developed scrapie in certain flocks, but not in others. There it was decided to slaughter all affected flocks and restock from scrapie-free flocks. All that happened was that new sheep put on to land where there had originally been scrapie also developed the disease. Again it was as if there was an environmental factor that actually triggered the disease. It was already well known that British flocks could go for many years without any cases of scrapie, only for several to occur within a short period of each other. Traditionally this was thought to be brought in from outside, and farmers regarded their flocks as scrapie-free if they had not had a recent case.

In the 1930s an extraordinary discovery was made:

scrapie could be transmitted from one animal to another by inoculating a small amount of infected tissue into the eye of another animal. The subject, sheep or goat, developed scrapie about a year later. By the time that I started looking into it scrapie had been transmitted experimentally to numerous other species in this way, and by 1988 many of the transmissions had also been demonstrated by feeding infected tissue to other animals. But where are these inoculations taking place in nature, since sheep are herbivores? Why does the infectivity not just disappear when the animal dies?

So here was a natural disease of sheep that appeared to depend on an environmental factor, seemed to require a genetic element, and was apparently transmissible by inoculation – a bizarre disease indeed. I began to see why so many different researchers had so many different ideas about it. In fact, most of the research into TSEs has been done with scrapie. It can be transmitted to mice and hamsters, which means that laboratory experiments can be undertaken cheaply and conveniently rather than large flocks of relatively slow-maturing sheep.

The Bovine Spongiform Encephalopathy Order 1988 Statutory Instrument 1039

21 June 1988 all cases of possible BSE had to be notified to MAFF.

The prohibition of the feeding of any ruminant protein to ruminants (NB this did not just apply to cattle) was introduced on 18 July 1988. The reason for the delay between the two parts of this order was to allow stocks of feed containing meat and bone meal to be cleared. It was MAFF's responsibility that this was adequate and that it was enforced.

Transmissible mink encephalopathy (TME) was a strange phenomenon that came under investigation in the 1960s, according to the information I could find.

14

Mink are vicious and on fur farms are caged individually to prevent them from damaging each other's fur. When a mink farm became affected it appeared that all or nearly all of the mink would die within a few months. Each would go through a period of mental degeneration in which their movements would become abnormal, they would chase their tails endlessly and then die. Two details indicated that the mink had become infected through eating scrapie in their feed. Firstly, the mink were separated from their mother and siblings when young, so they were unlikely to have infected each other; and secondly, the appearance of the brain was similar to that of scrapie, which it was known by then could be transmitted in food. Mink are fed on meat from the nearest available source. The problem was that there were not large numbers of sheep – and therefore of sheep carcasses – in the areas of the USA where the TME cases were appearing, so it seemed unlikely that contaminated food was the culprit. The disease could be produced artificially, however, by inoculating scrapie into a mink or by feeding it adequate amounts of scrapie brain, so the possibility could not be ruled out. The additional fact that a very large proportion of the mink on a farm were affected was to be of considerable interest – and concern – to me when I came to look at the statistics for BSE.

William Hadlow from Montana decided that it was worthwhile finding just how much transmissible mink encephalopathy (TME) infection was present in a mink during the disease's incubation period.

This took a lot of mink and a lot of time. A small amount of the disease was inoculated through the skin of a number of animals, which were then tested until they died of TME to see where the infection went. Initially it only seemed to go to the lymph glands near to the injection point. After that it appeared in the spleen and the brain. Unlike in other species it did not seem to be present in very high concentrations (a million times less than in hamsters). The mink did in fact die of

disease but fairly shortly after the infectivity appeared in many of their tissues.
This was just the sort of result that would be required for BSE for asymptomatic
cattle to be declared no danger to humans, and everyone had their fingers crossed.
Journal of Virology, October 1987.

Lastly, chronic wasting disease of deer (CWDD) was first noticed at a zoo park at Fort Collins in Colorado, and in the course of research had been transmitted to ferrets by inoculation. Again there was no information as to where the disease had come from, and the conclusion was drawn that it was caused naturally.

The infective unit (IU) and the incubation period

The technology developed in the period 1960–80 allowed research to be begun into the level of infectivity of the scrapie agent in the different tissues of an infected animal. This was done by a process known as serial dilution – by diluting a suspension of the tissue by 10 and assuming that the resulting fluid would have only one tenth as much infection per millilitre (ml) as the original suspension. This would be diluted by 10 again and so on until, for example, the final dilution would contain only one thousand millionth of the amount of tissue there had been at the start.

If a small amount of these diluted fluids were then inoculated into the brain of an animal, the expectation would be that the most concentrated amounts would infect the animal within a short incubation period (ip); as the fluid or inoculum becomes more dilute the incubation period would become longer and eventually there would be so little infective material present that effectively there would not be enough to infect the animal at all. With a little mathematics it can be worked out just how much infection was present in the tissue at the start. If, for instance, the fluid diluted one million times would infect the animal, but the fluid diluted 10 million times would not, then there was just enough to cause the infection in the one million dilution test; the amount inoculated was called one infective unit (IU). It follows that before the dilution took place there must have been 1 million infective units per ml in the original tissue. It was found that scrapie-infected brain tissue often contained 1000 million IU per gram. That means that there was enough in a single gram of brain tissue to infect one thousand million other animals! Other tissues, however, often contained a much lower level: the spleen, for instance, might contain only 10 million IU per gram, and muscle tissue only 10 IU per gram.

It was quickly discovered that the incubation period too would vary according to the amount of infective units inoculated. The more the test animal received, the shorter the incubation period. It was even possible to measure the amount of infectivity present in some tissue by inoculating an animal and measuring the incubation period. This, however, could only really indicate that if a small enough amount was inoculated the animal might possibly die of old age before the symptoms appeared! This theory is apparently still under argument.

It was also discovered that the infective agent responsible was very difficult to destroy. Boiling made little difference to it, household and most commercial cooking temperatures certainly would not, but autoclaving (heating to temperatures of about 135°C) did seem to have an effect. One researcher actually tried incinerating it, but found infection still present in the ash afterwards. Attempts at chemical destruction of the agent also seemed to be tough going. Strong acids, powerful disinfectants and solvents made little difference. Strong alkalis did seem to have an effect, but were unreliable. Enzymes that would destroy DNA or RNA were ineffective. Irradiation and ultraviolet light also appeared to leave the agent untouched, which was difficult to reconcile with the original idea that it was a viral disease. When the agent was buried in soil and left for three years the infection remained – almost all organic chemicals are destroyed by the action of soil bacteria, so this was indeed strange.

Dr Helen Grant, the neuropathologist from Charing Cross Hospital, wrote to *The Times* in spring 1989 following the Government's assurance to the public that BSE posed no risk to humans: 'This view is highly irresponsible and dangerous. The fact is that there may be a risk to humans: indeed some of us may already be incubating this fatal dementia.'

DNA and RNA are the nucleic acids that made up the genes of the cell. They carry the code that decides the structure of proteins that are made. Small changes in this structure can cause a major change in the shape of a protein and hence a change in the DNA of a cell can make it more or less easily infected with a TSE.

Viruses and prions

One particularly interesting finding was that it was possible to filter the infectivity out from a fluid. In other words, the agent was not a soluble chemical but a particle, and should therefore be discernible with the aid of an electron microscope . . . yet it wasn't. It is difficult to be certain; if one infective unit represents just one virus, then in the fine sliver of tissue under the microscope there might simply not be enough brain to contain any viruses. However, the scientific world has been looking for a long time, and could be expected to have seen the virus by now if it was there to be found.

Chemical methods of concentrating the infectivity from

brain tissue have produced interesting results: scrapie-associated fibrils (SAFs), found only in TSE-infected tissue, can then be seen under the electron microscope. They look like fibrils – tiny crystalloids, maybe only 100 microns long (a micron is one-millionth of a metre), which contain a specific piece of protein, known as the prion protein. Are these crystalloids in the cells normally, before the chemical concentration takes place? Is it just that we can't see them in that state? Are they anything to do with infectivity anyway? These questions were yet to be answered.

Harash Narang from Newcastle demonstrates electronmicroscopy as a method of diagnosis for animals infected with a TSE. *Proceedings of the National Academy of Science*, November 1987).

It was possible to look for the fine filaments that make up fibrils using electronmicroscopy, and this could be done in minutes. The test seemed to be fully sensitive and easy to carry out. His ideas were largely ignored by standard groups.

In 1980 Bolton and Prusiner, biochemical researchers in San Francisco, had carried out an important experiment. Working from the premise that there was infection present in tissue but that a virus could not be found, they proposed taking away from the infected tissue as many of its components as possible and then examining what remained to see if infectivity was still there . . . and what had not been destroyed. After treating some infective tissue with enzymes all that remained was a single group of proteins, which they believed must have something to do with infectivity. This conclusion has been contested ever since; various groups are still arguing about whether the protein, the above-mentioned prion, was implicated in the disease or was simply the result of a laboratory practice.

It was then found that the prion was made from a normal protein of the cell, named the prion protein – the reason for which the cell manufactured it, however, was unclear. It was found that certain tissues produced a lot of this prion protein and others almost none. The immune cells of the body and nerve cells were prolific, but many others did not bother to produce any at all.

Laura Manuelidis at Yale University showed that the prion protein might not be linked to the infection and that possibly it was nothing to do with prions at all. She found that the agent was not (whereas Prusiner's group in San Francisco had suggested that it was) completely resistant to being broken down by enzymes. When she removed some parts of the prion in a test tube this seemed to make no difference to the infectivity of the fluid in the tube. She found that it was possible to separate the prions from whatever were really the infective parts inside a test tube. She was convinced that the agent was like a virus and had its own nucleic acid, but was surrounded by membranes like the infected cell's own.

She knew that this virus would have to be unusual, for however hard they looked with an electron microscope scientists could not with certainty find classic virus-like particles. She also knew, however, that it was improbable that the prion would be different between strains of disease. If the prion was made from the normal protein of an infected animal, how could it have different strains of disease? Surely all the prions would be the same because they came from the same protein? This was a question that Prusiner currently could not answer by experiment and so relied on hypotheses to explain. *Journal of the European Molecular Biology Organisation*, February 1987.

It was also found that the body produced no antibodies to prions – presumably because they appeared just like a normal protein. This would explain why animals fail to build up any immunity to a TSE. It seems that the prions build up in the infected cells, and that they do so in parallel to the infectivity of the tissue – in other words, the more prions there are present, the higher the infectivity will be. Nervous cells just sit there and stay alive, whereas the immunity cells divide relatively frequently; it is therefore not surprising that the prions accumulate inside nervous cells and to a lesser extent in the immunity cells. After all, if the cell cannot destroy them, as it would a 'normal' virus, where can they go? There is some indication that the cells just push them out into the surrounding matter where they build up as a proteinaceous lump called an amyloid.

Harash Narang, from Newcastle Public Health Laboratory, reported that there may in fact be some DNA inside the infective agent of scrapie. He looked at extracts from infected brains and found that scrapie-associated fibrils could actually be changed by enzymes that destroyed DNA and be stained by colours that would only stain DNA. Maybe the prion idea was wrong? *Proceedings of the National Academy of Science,* May 1988.

It turned out that the scrapie-associated fibrils were partly composed of prion protein, and that many other factors pointed to the agent as the cause of the disease. But it was unclear just how this could be; nobody could see how a protein, made from a normal version of itself, could actually be responsible for infecting other cells. This was one of the questions that the individual research groups in scientific institutions around the world could not agree on.

The group of researchers based in Edinburgh were emphatic that there were variants of scrapie and that the infective agent could not therefore realistically all be formed only of the same protein. If that were the case, they implied, cases of scrapie would also always be the same. Another factor would be needed. Maybe a section of DNA? They called their agent the virino.

Other groups continued to feel that a virus would be found if we just looked hard enough for it. They had no faith in the idea that the prion could provide the entire answer, and were determined to look for aspects that the prion theory could not satisfy.

Undiagnosable, untreatable, fatal

What mattered to me, reading through the data, was that all the prion diseases were fatal (in a couple of cases vets claimed that a sheep had recovered, but there was no proof) after a very long incubation period. It was as if the agent built up slowly in the body to a level that caused severe damage to the nervous tissues, at which point symptoms would appear and the animal would die. Incubation periods in different animals varied: the longer the natural lifespan of the animal, the longer the infection period. Inevitably, however, the animal would die of a progressive degenerative nervous disease, in which the abilities required to carry out the basic functions needed to stay alive, such as eating and breathing, gradually disappeared.

At that time (and to this day) there was no method of treatment whatsoever for an animal with a TSE. Various things were being considered and were in the pipeline but none that had been tested (ionised polymers, amphoteracin B) was effective. Many of the research groups admitted that they simply did not know what the agent was; without that knowledge, how could they look for a treatment? Many drugs had been tried by neurologists in an attempt to treat human patients dying from CJD. Antiviral drugs made no difference, anti-inflammatory drugs were apparently valueless, and steroids got nowhere.

This was the prospect that had so worried the author of the article in the *BMJ* that was drawn to my attention that day in June 1988. If humans caught BSE from infected meat, there would be nowhere to turn.

The species barrier and transmission between species

Not only had no one succeeded in coming up with a successful cure for TSEs – there was not even a method of diagnosis for an animal that showed no signs of infection, except by injecting another animal with a sample of tissue and waiting to see if the second animal started to exhibit symptoms. A test of this kind might take a year or more, depending on which animals were being tested and which inoculated. If humans were already infected there would be no way of knowing until the symptoms started to appear. Indeed it might not realistically be possible to test any animal for infectivity by injecting tissue into one species from another because of what is known as the species barrier effect – when a TSE was transmitted experimentally from one species to another, it was widely recognised that a particularly large amount of infective agent was needed to effect this reliably. The problem was that the size of the barrier had not been quantified. It might be that the amount required to affect a mink was 10 times that required to infect a sheep, but perhaps 10,000 times as much again was needed to infect a monkey. This meant it would be impossible to be certain just how much BSE would be needed to infect a human by mouth, and it would be impossible to test BSE-infected cows for infectivity by inoculating the tissue into mice. So these experiments, which I presumed had already been started in 1988, would initially have to be carried out in cattle as well.

While there are now tests that take only a few hours to indicate whether we are infected with a virus like HIV, nothing comparable was found to indicate how many cattle (or indeed how many humans) were infected with BSE, whether the cattle slaughtered for our food were infected, or whether the cattle exported from the UK (at a rate of 450,000 per year) were. Such test procedures as there were simply could not be used to find out where the disease came from – whether most of the infected cattle ate cabbage leaves, for instance – or the numbers it would reach. There would be no way to find out if humans were being infected until they actually started to succumb to what would appear to be CJD, and even then we would have to wait until there had been a sufficiently significant rise in new CJD cases to show that the numbers were increasing nationally. If we were lucky, there would be a high species barrier between cattle and humans and we would have to eat so much beef to infect ourselves that it was in fact virtually impossible to do so.

However, without an effective diagnostic test we could not advise our trading partners that everything was all right with the beef we were sending them, and we could not tell our farmers, vets or butchers that they were not putting themselves at risk. We could not decide whether or not it was safe to eat beef – there was simply not enough information. However, we could make a good guess from the data on the TSEs in other species – which is what Dr Holt had done for his article in the *BMJ*.

TSE transmission in different animal species

Looking through the information about TSEs in other species, a few points became apparent which made it difficult for anyone to claim that we should not have to worry about BSE affecting ourselves. The first of these was that TSE agents were found in almost all the tissues of the body, although in some tissues they were several thousand times greater than in others. From Table 9 at the back of the book it can be seen that every area tested has shown infectivity in one animal or another, but that some tissues are much more prone to do so than others. The spleen and the brain are always infective, and the various organs that contain immune tissue (and hence immune cells) are very likely to be. It is also clear that some animals appear to have a lot more infectivity in their tissues than others. Mink, for instance, seemed to have relatively few IUs in the brain when tested in one experiment but when mouse brains were tested a large number were found. It was going to be difficult to predict just how much infectivity there would be in bovine tissues.

Something else that became clear was that if you inoculate an animal with the agent of a TSE it will show no symptoms for a long time; but that is not because there is no infection in its tissues. It just means that its brain has not yet been adequately destroyed to cause the clinical changes. Infectivity seems to start early in the peripheral tissues of the animal and only later in the nervous tissues, but it is still there long before the symptoms appear.

The two burning questions were these. Was it even possible that we could become infected from cattle that exhibited no symptoms? And could TSE be transmitted in food at all? The answers were clearly yes, it was possible (always assuming that BSE was capable of crossing the species barrier). It had even been worked out just how much tissue would be needed to transmit a TSE in this way – it seemed to me to be frighteningly little. One ten-thousandth of a gram of brain would be all that was needed, or a hundredth of a gram of spleen. Perhaps it might need 1000 grams of muscle or one gram of liver, but these did not seem to be unreasonable amounts. Many of the experiments had been carried out in mice, and it was difficult to get such a tiny animal to consume sufficiently large quantities of tissue. Humans, however, might eat hundreds of grams in a single meal. Could it be that a mouse might need a smaller amount because it was small and we would need a larger amount because we were large? These were the sort of questions yet to be answered, but generally in virology and bacteriology the size of the animal does not matter. The simple explanation is that the infection interacts with single cells, which are the same size whatever the size of the animal.

> Shirou Mohri in Japan tried taking out the thymus and spleen (both important for immunity) from a mouse and then injecting the animals with scrapie. She found that neither of the organs made any appreciable difference. In other words since animals did not produce any antibodies to scrapie, it was difficult to see any immunity to the disease being gained by the body. It seemed that if you gave enough scrapie to a susceptible animal it would develop the disease and could not become immune.
>
> One of the most important things to come out of this was that TSEs might be cumulative. In other words you could inject small amounts every day and if they added up to enough over, say, a month, the total would be sufficient to cause the disease.
>
> The worry about BSE was, of course, that we would be eating small, possibly insignificant, amounts of it on different days. As our bodies could not destroy the agent, nor did animals seem to excrete it, and no immunity was formed, then it might be assumed that it would just build up. *Journal of General Virology*, 1987.

At that time it was not at all clear just how much scrapie was needed to infect a cow by mouth – there wasn't even any evidence that scrapie had infected cattle at all. It was just a reasonable idea at the time. Nor was there yet any idea of how much infection was contained in bovine tissues – so trying to work out how much infectivity we were likely to be eating was not possible, never mind working out how much would be needed to infect us. The more I read, the more I realised just how much of a risk was being taken at that time. There was no public announcement that there was a risk at all and presumably this was justified by the lack of proof that any human beings at all would be affected. Then again, there was no evidence that we would not be at risk – and should this turn out to be the case the result would be catastrophic for the country.

I sorted my way through all the data about scrapie and CJD that had appeared over the previous 20 years and realised that some researchers had put their whole lives into the subject. Ian Pattison, an expert from MAFF, turned up again and again for instance. Scientists had already tried inoculating animals with scrapie – everything from rats to cats. CJD had also been inoculated into many animals, from monkeys to ferrets. When I looked hard, I could work out just how many different attempted transfers had been successful – about 70% of the possibilities. (see Table 3).

The slow race for the truth

The excitement for the microbiologists of the nineteenth century must have been intense. Ross and Koch were investigating malaria, a subject of international importance. Pasteur and Jenner had opportunities to destroy other diseases that had killed vast numbers. Now researchers in various parts of the world are battling with the chemistry and microbiology of TSEs. If there is only one thing I am sure of in all this, whatever the rights and wrongs, it is that the researchers into TSEs are both brilliant and dedicated and that the cocktail of single-mindedness and competition will get them to the answer in the end.

Meanwhile, from what I was reading, some factors did not seem to have been adequately investigated. They were not part of the big race for scientific supremacy and were perhaps therefore felt to be of minor importance. For instance, were TSEs cumulative? The agent, whatever it was, was absorbed into the body, could not be destroyed and was apparently not excreted, so maybe it did accumulate. There were no antibodies against it or immune

27

reaction to it, so it might well sit in the body untouched. When I asked one of the research scientists about this, he replied that the assumption was that it was cumulative and it was felt unnecessary to carry out experiments to which they thought they already knew the answers. But I wanted to know whether small quantities that were individually not enough to infect an animal could add up if given separately on different days. It seemed very likely, but there was as yet no proof.

What effect might the immense amounts of drugs now used in humans and animals have? Could they be a factor? And what was the environmental factor involved in scrapie? Surely this was important; it either caused the disease or allowed its symptoms to come through and, as every pharmaceutical company knows, if you can identify the cause you can look for the cure.

In 1988 the fiercest arguments were raging over the nature of the infective agent in TSEs, and intense research was being carried out in this area. BSE made its entry in the middle of all this and MAFF immediately initiated some research into the epidemiology of the disease. Where did it come from? Was it linked to injections? Was it transferred between cattle in the field? The various researchers in the field of TSEs in the UK jumped at the idea of working on BSE – but there was not yet any funding to do so. They were going to have to wait for the report of a government committee, set up in 1987 and chaired by Richard South-wood, Professor of Biology at Oxford, to find out what money might be available. This report, requested by MAFF and the Department of Health (DoH), was expected in 1988. It would – at least so everyone hoped – recommend what research should be carried out and how it should be funded. It never arrived; at least, it was not published then.

Concerned by the apparent omissions, I sat down and tried to work out what data would be needed to work out the risks of BSE to humans. The first thing that was starkly clear to me was that by the time the research had been carried out it would already be too late to take the necessary preventative action.

The kind of research expected

If a new infective disease such as BSE appears – fatal, with no known treatment and a very long incubation period – we have to find out if humans are susceptible. For ethical reasons we can't deliberately inject it into someone and wait to see if he or she catches it, and we can't just wait to see whether people catch it by accident, because by the time the number of cases of CJD rises significantly it will be too late to do anything about it. So what can we do?

1. Can humans can be infected at all? There's no hard scientific way of producing an answer to this. All we can do to produce an estimate of risk is to inoculate as many different species as possible with BSE. If it turns out that only 25 out of 100 species tested go down, I would assume that there was similarly a 25% chance that humans can be infected. I realise this will not be popular with those against animal research, but sometimes the ends justify the means.

2. How much infectivity is needed to pass the disease to humans? This would have to be assessed by finding out how much infectivity there is in one particular tissue at the same time as feeding many different species varying amounts of infectivity. The mouse might need to eat 10^5 infective units, the monkey 10^7 IU, the cat 10^6 IU and so on. At the end of the experiment we would have an approximate idea that, if we could be infected at all, we would need to eat, say, between 10^4 and 10^9 IU.

No surprise was shown that BSE existed. After all, all other domestic ruminants were affected by a TSE. But why should it appear now? Maybe it was because of the change in offal rendering that took place at the beginning of the 1980s? Maybe there has been a change in scrapie? Maybe it is a new strain of scrapie?

Yes, said this editorial, the precautions of destroying most animals with symptoms have been carried out, but what about those infected but without symptoms?

Will we be able to control the herds with the disease while paying the farmer only 50% compensation? The author doubted it, from his knowledge of farmers. He estimated that it would cost £40 million to slaughter all the cattle on infected farms in the UK and restart. He thought that the farmers would not let the bloodstock from years of breeding go so easily.

He said it was important to make a commitment to provide funds not only to research the 'what is?' of BSE but also the 'what if?' In other words, we should start worrying. 'BSE and scrapie: agents of change', *Lancet* editorial, 10 September 1988.

3. How much infectivity is there in the tissues that we eat from cattle? This would be done initially by inoculating the brains of cattle with varying amounts of tissue from an infected cow. We might find, for instance, that there are only 10 IU per gram in meat (muscle tissue), but 10^8 IU per gram in the brain. If we could show that mice were sensitive enough to the disease we could do some of the experiments on laboratory mice.

4. What proportion of cattle are infected? This would require over a hundred samples of the brain of cattle at slaughterhouses to be inoculated, separately, into the brains of other cattle.

5. Is BSE passed from cow to calf (this is known as vertical transmission)? We would need a group of calves that are the offspring of cattle with BSE, and a control group whose mother was not infected. Then it would be a case of waiting to see if the calves developed BSE over the next few years.

In mid-1988, when I was first alerted to the existence of BSE by the *BMJ* article, I expected that these experiments would have already been started. It turned out that by 1995 none except the last had been adequately put into motion.

The MAFF response to food scares

My then boss, Richard Lacey, was Professor of Microbiology at Leeds University. Regarded by MAFF as a mad scientist from the north of England who did not know enough about the subjects he complained about, he was put down by government officers as an ignorant man who just liked being on television. Lacey put up with this because he tended to get things done despite the best efforts of officialdom. He was popular with the media, as he made good television which they could show as news.

> Jim Hope in Edinburgh notices that there are scrapie-associated fibrils (SAFs) in the brain of cattle with BSE, and also that they are made of the prion protein. In other words, BSE is just like all the other TSEs in the way it grows. *Nature*, September 1988.

We had recently been involved in the listeria problem and the outbreaks of salmonella. Lacey had complained about the introduction of BST (bovine somatotropin, a hormone for farmers to inject into their cattle to produce more milk), the introduction of cook-chill foods into institutions, and the use of ionising radiation to preserve food (to name but a few of his concerns). He was just the person to pick up on the threat of BSE.

> Manuelidis from Yale reported the transmission of Alzheimer's disease from the blood of humans to animals. These experiments will need to be repeated, as other attempts to transmit the disease from the brain were unsuccessful. *Proceedings of the National Academy of Science,* 1988.

Humphery-Smith from Brest (France) demonstrated that spiorplasmas, single-celled organisms, could infect animal brains to produce an encephalopathy and look like the scrapie-associated fibrils found in scrapie. *Lancet*, November 1988.

After he had made some pertinent remarks about listeria the media had asked the Central Public Health Laboratory for information. The expert there told them, truthfully, that there had been a sevenfold rise in disease due to listeria over the previous 15 years and that in other countries some outbreaks had been due to the bacterium being in food. The newspapers loved it, and by the next morning questions were being asked in the House of Commons.

Within a few days, however, MAFF had demanded that CPHL should not give information about food, even about food poisoning (it is the major government department in the UK concerned with food poisoning outbreaks). Initially, information reached the press that listeria did not cause disease at all; a few days later it was admitted that yes, it did cause a small amount of disease, but not associated with food. Still later it was admitted that it was associated with food but never in the UK. Eventually it was admitted that there had been an outbreak in the UK as well – but by that time the scare had subsided and the press were no longer interested.

The Ministry of Agriculture, Fisheries and Food (MAFF) was originally principally the Ministry of Agriculture but it took over other responsibilities later. At the top, the adviser to the Government is the Chief Veterinary Officer (currently Keith Meldrum), and under him is a large bureaucratic machine. Through organising by statute MAFF can direct the ways in which British agriculture works, and as a result it has been one of the major causes of the huge rise in UK agricultural output since 1945. We now export many of the foods for which we were once dependent on other countries. The scientists who work for

MAFF are highly qualified but have been under extreme pressure for several years: more and more veterinary laboratories have been closed and their staff made redundant.

This was to be the pattern followed by MAFF for every food-related scare – initial denial followed by gradual admission of minimal risk. To do this effectively, they had to make sure that external experts were not available to give conflicting information to the media. This could be done in a number of ways. They could make sure that they were the only place with experts and infer that other sources were invalid. They could be advised by specific groups such as the Southwood Committee, in whose selection they had some influence and to whom only they could provide the information with which to make decisions; this group could then be quoted as an independent source of information while MAFF could claim merely to be doing what they were advised. The next thing was not to carry out research that would go against them for external scientific publications. In addition they would provide the media with large quantities of data, much of which could not be used and would need an expert to interpret for the layman.

It is admittedly difficult to know what should be done by a government agency when confronted by this sort of information reaching the media. If they admit that accusations are likely to be true, it is like saying that they should, for instance, have tested cook-chill food themselves and set up procedures to deal with it, and an industry which had been producing income, employment and taxes virtually grinds to a halt. Yet if they deny things that are later proved well-founded they may in the long run be perceived as misleading the public, who will gradually stop believing what they say.

Congratulations to the group from the Central Veterinary Laboratory, including John Wilesmith, for carrying out the excellent epidemiological work within one year and finding out so much about the new disease BSE. It indicates that it is caused by scrapie in bovine food, and got over the species barrier by being there in such quantity. Feed including ruminant protein was stopped in July 1988 but a drop in BSE should not be expected until 1992. Taking an optimistic view, the disease will be insignificant by 1995. Editorial in the *Veterinary Record*, December 1988.

With BSE, however, matters were different in that effective action could only be taken to avoid risk to humans before proof of human risk was available. In other words denial was a very easy option and would be the one that everyone would like to hear. The actual assessment of risk, and the action necessary to minimize it, was just so enormous that it could not be contemplated; and having told everyone that there was no proof and so they shouldn't worry, the Government would have to sanction the slaughter of large parts of the UK dairy herd, demonstrating just how worried they were.

BSE should in reality have been one of the first of the food 'scares'. Details reached the *Veterinary Record* in 1987, but it came in with a whimper rather than a bang – it passed almost unnoticed by the press. It was only when Helen Grant and Professor Lacey decided that it was of much greater significance that the media started to sit up and take notice, in 1988 and 1989. By this time, however, MAFF knew how to handle things. It decided to take the denial approach, and information was given to the press from a controlled source at Whitehall.

£527,142 was paid to farmers in compensation for BSE in 1988.

A MAFF news release dated 19 February 1988 announced the following compensation figures per animal for cattle accepted by their veterinary officers as possibly having BSE: £654 if BSE is confirmed by post-mortem, £818 if BSE is not confirmed. These figures were based on the average market price for a Friesian cow and heifer in milk, which was £645.82, and new prices were decided every month.

The price was, however, agreed between the veterinary officer and the farmer at the time that the VO visited, and may not have been as high as this.

It was clear to me that direct information about BSE was not reaching the medical literature and that what we were hearing was what MAFF was allowing us to hear. On a visit to the Central Public Health Laboratory (CPHL) I went to ask their epidemiological group what was going on. It was their job to record cases of disease that were relevant to human health and BSE was clearly within their brief. They had in fact started to look into it and to prepare reports of cases of BSE and CJD for doctors in the UK. It appeared, however, that this was then stopped from above. They were told that CPHL should have nothing to do with BSE and that all that information should come entirely from MAFF.

Scott from Edinburgh wrote in 1989 in the *Journal of the American Veterinary Association* how BSE could be diagnosed by looking at the symptoms and signs of the living cow. It had difficulty standing, was continuously afraid and apprehensive, and had changes in its brain waves that you could measure electrically. He warned that this could happen to other countries unless they were careful. To him it was fully evident that BSE had come from scrapie and that the UK was the country with the problem because we had so many sheep. But that did not mean that it could not get out of the UK, and everyone was afraid of that.

'But we know what will happen,' said one of the experts. 'MAFF will assume that humans are not at risk until there's actual proof that they are.'

'We've seen it so many times before,' added another, 'and it's the opposite of what should be done. You have to assume that humans are at risk until they are shown not to be.'

'There's no way MAFF would accept something like that,' I said. 'That would mean mass slaughter of cattle and would be completely unacceptable to the industry. They know they have to take a certain risk with human lives, and they'll try to keep this acceptably low without ruining the beef and dairy industries.'

In the UK 60% of the cattle are derived from milking herds, but only 2% of young calves are sold at home. Every milking cow is expected to produce approximately four offspring, and clearly one of these four will have to replace her when she is slaughtered at the end of her seven-year milking life. Artificial insemination is almost universal now and the type of sire (bull) can be decided by the farmer. Two out of the four inseminations will be from a bull of a milking breed; one of the two calves produced will be female and the other will be male. This male calf will not produce large amounts of beef and is generally exported to Europe for veal. The other two calves are derived from semen from a beef-breed sire and can be slaughtered as bullocks and heifers, between the ages of one and three years. The system is highly efficient while there remains a market for veal calves, and milk production in the UK has been a profitable business, particularly with EC subsidies.

'So how are they going to judge what's acceptably low?' he asked. 'The risk from listeria was low – only a few hundred cases a year – but when you gave the information to the population pregnant women avoided eating cook-chill food and it was a good thing too. The risk from whooping cough vaccine was minimal – one per hundred thousand – but the mother would rather risk school friends infecting her children with whooping cough than deliberately put them at risk. The calculated risk from BSE can't be nailed down at the moment, and by the time we find out what the risk actually is in 20 years' time it will be too late to do anything about it. Surely this is a major communicable disease which should be discussed by the medical profession? Why are we being manipulated like this?'

Taylor in Edinburgh was asked to write an article for the *Veterinary Record* about scrapie decontamination and its implications for BSE. A very depressing paper.

He admitted that the agent was very resistant to heat. 100°C was certainly not enough to destroy it and autoclaving at 134°C for 18 minutes would be required with longer periods if lower temperatures were used. He also admitted that chemicals did not seem to have much effect on scrapie infectivity either. Formaldehyde and ordinary disinfectants were valueless. Domestic bleach had to be used in high concentrations and would cause severe metal corrosion if used in that way. Acids did not seem to be effective. Sodium hydroxide (washing soda) might disinfect a surface if left there for an hour, but this was contradicted by another researcher whom he quoted. By the end of his article he could offer no perfect advice.

He knew that renderers are bound to be sent infected material; should it be to make a fast penny or innocently, it was bound to happen. He made it clear that cutting down the amount of infection arriving at the renderers seemed to be the only way of stopping contamination of meal. *Veterinary Record*, March 1989.

As this was being published MAFF were issuing guidelines on decontamination of abattoirs and other places where BSE might cause a problem. It is unlikely that their methods could be thought either fully effective or tested. Two years later Taylor told me that there was almost no way of getting rid of BSE except by burning it. This is still true in 1996.

'Because quite simply if you advised medics – never mind the public – that there was a risk of unknown magnitude from eating beef you'd crash the meat trade the next day, I should think.' I put it over a bit hard. 'After the other scares I'm sure that MAFF are determined to handle this themselves. Anyway, my feeling is that MAFF probably think they're doing the right thing, and don't want another government agency giving information that might conflict with theirs.'

'But if we don't provide this sort of information, who will?'

That was a hard one. They were a very professional, helpful crew who were proud of the help they provided to the country's doctors in avoiding major outbreaks – theirs was an essential job. It seemed to me that stifling them was not in anyone's interest. On the train back from London to Leeds I sat and thought about what I should do. Taking advantage of a captive audience, I explained the problem to a lecturer from Scotland who was sitting opposite me.

'There's simply nothing that I can do personally,' I said. 'After all, who am I? The changes in the NHS are making it more and more difficult to get a consultant's post and the one person they don't want is someone who rocks boats.'

'Do you see yourself as a boat rocker?' he asked.

'Not really. I'm actually extremely easy-going and I work very hard. I care about my patients and I'm fascinated by my research. I've got on well with the technical staff everywhere I've worked, and the medics too on the whole. I've worked in thirty hospitals in nine countries.'

'But who *is* going to tell the public about BSE? What about the countries to which we export our meat? What about the next generation of people whose parents may die before they're middle-aged? What about the country generally if things go wrong?' He was getting warmed to the subject. 'How many other groups in the UK either know enough about the subject to realise that the risk is unacceptably high, or can get that through to the media? How many are actually willing to do it?'

'You're saying that, as nobody else will make a stand, I

ought to?' I asked. 'Even though I don't carry much weight, so I can't take any great stand?'

'Either that or you can do what they're doing, look back in 20 years to see if you did the right thing in 1988 and remember to blame yourself if people died.' I wondered if he was from the Philosophy Department.

In the end I found that medical involvement in assessing BSE risks to humans had been taken out of (or kept from) the hands of the environmental health groups, the public health departments, the CPHL, the Royal Colleges (of Medicine, Dietetics, Nursing and so on). The British Medical Association had no policy on BSE, and many other independent groups automatically believed the information that came from MAFF on the subject.

CHAPTER TWO

Southwood and the arrival of officialdom

At the end of 1988 we were waiting for the report of the government's Working Party on Bovine Spongiform Encephalopathy, to be known as the Southwood Report. It soon became clear, however, that information would be kept well under wraps even though the report was largely ready. Meetings on the subject would be private (although various observers would be present), and it was going to be difficult for the rest of us to find out what was going on. All we could do was wait until the Government eventually did decide to publish the report, which it did on 3 February 1989, although it was only released to the press and the House of Commons after what may have been a number of major changes. MAFF, however, denies that such changes took place.

A good report is a bad report

Southwood, Professor of Zoology at Oxford, was thought of as an honest man. However, he and all the members of his committee, appointed by MAFF and the Department of Health, were quite elderly and only Professor Epstein was a virologist. The lack of a presence in the working party of anyone from the sphere of medical ethics, and the fact that the source of almost all the information provided to it was

MAFF, were worrying at the time. Major researchers on scrapie and BSE in the UK were not asked for their opinion on the subject, and much of the information on spongiform encephalopathies were taken out of good textbooks.

Despite this the report is initially excellent, giving specific definitions of the disease, as a transmissible spongiform encephalopathy affecting cattle generally between the ages of 3 and 11 years. It gave quite good clinical descriptions of the symptoms in cattle and of the way these symptoms appeared to accelerate when stressed. It described the origins of the disease and the method by which it is transferred between animals. But there was bad news too (for those of us who wanted to know the truth). The report also stated that BSE was most unlikely to have any implications for human health – that the risk of transmission to humans 'appears remote'. However, it went on 'Nevertheless, if our assessments of these likelihoods are incorrect, the implications would be extremely serious'.

Major findings and recommendations of the Southwood Report

- BSE was likely to be a 'dead end host' (in other words, other species would not become infected from cattle)
- the carcasses of clinically infected cattle should be destroyed
- there should be a ban on ruminant-based protein in rations for ruminants, and this should continue indefinitely
- direct inoculations of bovine-based tissue into humans should stop
- safe working practices should be drawn up by the Health and Safety Executive for people working with infected cattle and tissue
- milk from infected cattle should be destroyed
- products for human food containing brain or spleen should be labelled as such
- baby food manufacturers should avoid the use of bovine brain, thymus and other offal

---

In 1994 the Department of Health asked that people that had received human growth hormone should not donate blood because of the very remote risk of CJD being present in the blood.

This was worse than we had imagined. How had the members of the working party come up with this? Clearly BSE, like other TSEs, would be transmissible to other animals and not a 'dead-end host'. Surely they had no grounds for thinking otherwise? There was certainly data showing that when a TSE passed from one animal to another it became less infective, but this was small print and would need to be retested before it could be accepted as fact. The report seemed to give the impression that cattle without symptoms would consequently not be infective. That was undeniably absurd. If one thing was sure, it was that infectivity in tissues of TSE-infected animals appeared long before the symptoms. This was a fatal disease, with no treatment and no means of diagnosis, cases of which were rising rapidly in numbers throughout the UK. Yet a major working party had come to the conclusion that it was safe to permit it to be fed to humans, even though it was aware that all members of this group of diseases could be transmitted by mouth.

The report of the epidemiology showed BSE to be a classic result of an extended common source outbreak: in other words it started in one place and spread from there to other farms and animals round about, but could spread a long way also. There was no evidence of cattle-to-cattle transmission, but it would have been very difficult at the time to show this. Similarly there was no evidence of transmission from mother to calf, but again it would have been almost impossible to have had such information due to the very long incubation period of the disease. Some 75% of affected herds at that time had only suffered a single case. The committee could not show any association between the disease and various chemicals used on the cattle (including organophosphorous insecticides), nor could they find any association with vaccines or other chemicals used on farms that might get into the feed. It seemed impossible that sheep with scrapie could be a specific cause of the disease either, since only 20% of the affected farms had any sheep.

The only common feature in all cases was the use of commercial concentrates for feed. This suggested that meat and bone meal was the cause of the disease, and that different suppliers of the meal ran different risks of producing infected food. Computer analysis showed that both calves and adults might have been exposed to infected meal, but the risk of actually developing BSE was 30 times higher for calves than for adult cattle. The maximum incubation period that could be observed in 1987 was six years, suggesting that initial infection had taken place in about 1981.

The committee decided that the reason why the epidemic might well have started in 1981–2 was that it coincided with the change from one method of fat extraction during the rendering process (using acetone) to another (using just heat). One of the products of this process was the meat and bone meal which was used as a protein supplement in cattle feed. In fact the new style of processing had been used since the mid-1970s for 20% of the meat and bone meal produced.

Some information in the document was actually incorrect – for instance, claims that transfer of TSEs between individual mice did not occur. In fact this had been reported. Apart from the major recommendations (see box) the report also suggested that we should check whether the incidence of Creutzfeldt-Jakob disease was increasing.

By that time there had already been a ban on cattle with

43

BSE symptoms being eaten, and their carcasses had to be destroyed. Milk from cattle suspected of being infected had to be destroyed. All this seemed reasonable, but a few other factors were not. The report stated that cattle with symptoms should be destroyed – but what about the ones without symptoms? As any of the researchers in the subject will say, the difference in infectivity between the two groups may well not be great. Surely if one group was worth slaughtering the other group could not be ignored? This omission may well have been the result of changes, at the behest of MAFF, between the production of the report and its publication.

The report also suggested that there would be a total of around 17,000–20,000 cases. But at the time the available data was simply not good enough to enable anyone to make such precise predictions. It even said that the disease would have a very low incidence by 1996 – clearly an untenable suggestion even at that time. The committee also seemed happy that the disease would reach a 'dead end' in cattle, with no other animals becoming infected from them. This was an extremely optimistic statement to make back in early 1989. Epidemiological calculation of the number of infected cases that had already been eaten could have been attempted at that time; but it was not. Risk levels for humans could have been attempted by looking at the general ability of TSEs to be transmitted from one species to another; if this data was indeed looked at, little heed seems to have been taken of it.

One of the major results of the Southwood Report was the setting up of the Spongiform Encephalopathy Advisory Committee (SEAC), also known as the Tyrrell Committee. Again, members were appointed by government agencies and none of the members came from the field of medical ethics.

The general feeling from the Southwood Report was that the committee were clearly willing to take a chance with human lives and must have felt the risk low enough to be acceptable. In other words they were taking the most optimistic scenario at every turn. In Professor Lacey's opinion they did not have enough data to justify it and certainly not enough to be sure. I suggested I should visit the experts in both Britain and the USA to find out more about what was going on in the research field.

CHAPTER THREE

At the cutting edge of research

The information that hit the press in 1988 and 1989 had made us wonder what was going on. Professor Lacey, now sure that MAFF were not to be relied upon, was probably going to take them on concerning BSE. It was clear that research had been going on into scrapie in the UK for the last 50 years, but neither Lacey nor I knew enough about the subject. I would have to get myself up to the level of the research scientists around the world before the media could be confronted properly. In the summer of 1989 I gave myself a month to do that, on both sides of the Atlantic.

Karen Hsiao showed that a change in the gene for the prion protein was found in patients with the Gerstmann-Straussler-Scheinker syndrome. In other words a mutation in a single gene seemed to cause it by making what was a normal prion protein change into a prion. These patients did not seem to be infected from an outside source at all, and they passed the disease to half of their offspring. Such a classic familial disease must surely be due to genetic changes. This stood well for Bolton and Prusiner's theory that the infectious agents that caused TSEs were just the prions, which were themselves derived from the body's own proteins. *Nature*, 23 March 1989.

North of the border

Richard Kimberlin, whose name cropped up again and again in the scientific literature, is the Edinburgh-based

46

expert who organised much of the work on the growth of infective agent in animals. He showed how the agent was passed along nerves, how it was found in large amounts in different tissues, and how infectivity took place. His work at Edinburgh University's Neuropathogenesis Unit was largely funded by the Agriculture and Food Research Council (AFRC). When AFRC ran out of money to support this expensive facility, Kimberlin became an independent adviser on BSE to the food industry.

Although not a member of the Southwood Committee, he was quickly put on the Tyrrell Committee. As soon as his foot was in the door he demanded that the tissues found to be most highly infective in other animals should be removed from human food; Southwood did not seem to accept that asymptomatic cattle should be assumed to be infective.

Sklaviadis at Yale had tried to take the prion to pieces and see if infectivity remained. He took some infected brain, and extracted various fractions with different methods. Then he had to find out if the most infectivity was in the same fraction as the most prions. He found that it was not. So perhaps just because there are a lot of prions in a sample does not mean that it is infectious at all? He found that the most infectivity was in the fraction that carried the most particulate matter and DNA. So maybe the infective agent was really a particle with some DNA inside – a virus. *Journal of Virology*, March 1989.

Casaccia in Rome found that hamsters that had been inoculated with scrapie were found to have the disease in their blood throughout the incubation period. This was not so surprising, but suggested that asymptomatic humans or cattle might also have the infection in their blood. *Archives of Virology*, 1989.

In the history of the research into scrapie Kimberlin had been the man behind the virino. It was his idea that the agent was in fact a small piece of nucleic acid wrapped in a proteinaceous cover. This allowed him to explain the different strains of disease that seemed to have appeared. He reasoned that if the disease was purely due to a single type of protein, derived from the genes of the animal, how could it differ in the strains of disease? He was convinced, and produced scientific research to support his argument, that the agent remains the same in the different species that were infected. Therefore if BSE was derived from scrapie, then when sheep were deliberately infected with BSE they would get scrapie – and one particular strain of disease at that. If that was true then it would be hoped – as scrapie did not infect humans, and BSE and scrapie were one and the same – that BSE would not infect humans either. This may well be a welcome view to have on a committee advising the Government, if the Government want to be told that there was no risk from BSE.

Judd Aiken felt that there might be an association between mitochondria (the power producers of the cell) and the agent of scrapie. He was saying that inside an infected cell the agent might be connected to them – indeed, he found a better association between infection and the mitochondria than with the prion protein. *Journal of Virology*, April 1989.

When the Southwood Report came out Professor Lacey had, not unexpectedly, fired some warning shots about BSE via the media. During a fairly amicable discussion Kimberlin asked me: 'Can't you calm your professor down? He's repeatedly saying things that there simply isn't enough data to justify.'

I reminded him how often Lacey had been proved right in the past, but added that I would try to put it to him that the removal of contaminated feed from cattle in 1988 should have stopped the whole thing.

'Well, he's doing a lot more harm than good. MAFF doesn't listen to hysterical media, it listens to farmers. MAFF is made up of vets who have connections throughout the farming world. Farmers are their friends and they think Lacey's just raving.'

Kimberlin did not seem to be in MAFF's pocket, but rather someone who was determined to get things done as well as he could. I felt we should encourage him – anyone who stood up against MAFF would need people behind him telling him he was right.

When Kimberlin was put on the Tyrrell Committee he thought he would see something done, but he did not fully realise the way this type of committee is organised and to what extent it can be influenced by the government department in charge. He would have a harder time than he anticipated.

Also working in Edinburgh was Hugh Frazer, who ran a major research group on scrapie. Frazer, the expert in spongiform encephalopathies at the Neuropathogenesis Unit (NPU) at Edinburgh University, was accompanied by a senior colleague, Moira Bruce, when I met him.

Ron Davies (Caerphilly), Labour Front Bench Spokesman for Agriculture.

He had demanded to speak about BSE in the House of Commons and only got his chance at 12.38 am on 17th May 1989. I had provided him with quite a lot of serious information concerning the spread of this type of disease and how it is difficult to get rid of. He explained the disease to the House and went on to the problems that it might pose.

He told them that it spread through infested food and abraded skin, that it created no immunity, that it causes an undetectable disease until symptoms appeared.

He noticed that the Southwood committee had described the chance of BSE getting to humans as 'remote'. 'Which word, I wonder, would the Government have

---

> chosen in the early 1980s to describe the possibility of scrapie in sheep crossing to cattle?'
>
> He then described all the serious action that had been taken by the Government for a 'remote' chance. In fact the NFU had said their actions had been inadequate.
>
> He quoted neuropathologist Helen Grant saying that we simply could not know if we were eating potentially fatal doses of the disease or not and neither could the Government.

Apparently he had been called to give evidence by South-wood and was asked a few simplistic questions – things that were actually dealt with in standard textbooks. For some reason, however, the committee did not ask him for his opinion on numerous important subjects that were to be covered by the report. He was astonished, and it was clear that he regarded some of the points in the report as questionable.

Moira chipped in. 'I certainly wouldn't give my children any beef tissue if I thought it came from an infected cow.' She went on to indicate that she thought the action taken had been dreadful. Why had they not asked the experts? Why were they forcing specific research to be done when they all knew it was not going to work? Why was MAFF not showering them with funding for wider research?

> De Armond, a histopathologist working in San Francisco, found that where there were prions in the brain there was infectivity, but where the prions were fewer so was the infectivity. Yet another indication that the prions were closely associated with not just the damage that was done to the brain but also the ability to infect others. *Progress in Clinical Biology Research*, 1989.

'The thing is, Moira, how can we know which cattle are infected and which are not? Doesn't it seem difficult to justify eating any bovine tissue at all?' I asked the obvious question. The Southwood Report, of course, had simply proposed to destroy all cattle that showed signs of disease; others could be eaten at will.

'God knows! But whatever they do, they must first ask the experts whether it will work,' she replied.

Consultative Committee on Research into Spongiform Encephalopathies (Tyrrell Committee), June 1989

This was the committee's first report, and a fairly rapid one after the publication of the Southwood Report. One of its first suggestions, whether official or not, was that offals should be banned from human food. MAFF refused, then backed down, though insisting that liver and kidney, both of which had been shown in other TSEs to be infective, should be excluded from the ban. Feeling ran high that this decision was made purely because those offals had a specific price and would decrease abattoir income dramatically if they had to be disposed of. A cynical view, but it is difficult otherwise to see why neither was included in the ban.

Marion Winter, vet to a large herd in Surrey, noticed that a lot of the cattle were developing BSE. By June 1988 there had been 14 cases – the average on other farms was one or two. By the time I managed to get in touch with her in 1989 there were between 60 and 80 cases on the farm. The reason was uncertain. One of the most important parts of the article she wrote was that no protein of animal origin had been fed to either heifers or cows in the herd for the previous five years, and there had been no direct contact with sheep. Also important was that it was a very large herd with over 250 cows. The fact that it was so early in the epidemic was alarming. She told me that she had been put under pressure not to speak to the press. She said that the research group from Edinburgh had arrived to take electroencephalograms (brainwaves) of the cattle still alive, and that this was reasonable – after all, it could be a test of whether a cow was incubating the disease. All they had to do was take the measurements and then wait to see which cattle died of BSE. They were thrown off the farm, not by the owner but by a representative of MAFF, who demanded that the experiment be stopped. *British Veterinary Journal*, 1989.

It seemed that MAFF, who funded the NPU research into BSE, decided which experiments were to be carried out, and how. NPU staff realised that they would have to fight just to get the experiments carried out properly; MAFF was probably worried that if they gave these researchers *carte blanche* they might find out all sorts of things that MAFF simply did not want to know and definitely did not want the public to know.

Scott in San Francisco found that if the gene for the prion protein of a hamster was put into the genes of a mouse (called a 'transgenic mouse'), and if it was infected with scrapie, it would easily produce the prion that infected the hamster.

Usually an animal will produce a TSE that infects its own species more easily than any other, and a much larger dose has to be inoculated into another species in order to transmit it (the species barrier). What Scott found was that, if you put the hamster gene for the prion protein into the mouse, the mouse would be able to infect a hamster as if there were no species barrier.

This finding that the species barrier depended on the gene that decided the prion protein was important. It meant that the prion protein must be extremely important in the infection process.

Kimberlin from Edinburgh showed that the strain of scrapie kept its identity when the disease was transferred from a mouse to a hamster and then back to a mouse. This shows that the strain type is not decided by the genes of the animal that is infected but is carried by the infective agent. *Journal of General Virology*, 1989.

Hoping that MAFF would not succeed in this aim, I prepared to fly to America. The US research groups, particularly the San Francisco-based ones, took a different viewpoint from the NPU. Edinburgh was the centre for the theory that scrapie was caused by a virino (that is, with some of its own genes), while the USA was the focus for prion research (that is, involving no genetic material).

Dave Westaway from San Francisco wrote of the work that had been done into the genetics of prion diseases. They had looked at the genes for the normal prion protein in numerous animals and humans. What they found was that these genes were remarkably similar throughout the mammalian range that they tried. The gene was even found in much lower forms of life. When the gene changed, the incubation period changed after infection or, in humans, the disease might appear spontaneously. Surely the prion must be involved in the pathogenesis somehow? *Trends in the Neurosciences*, June 1989.

European Commission Decision 89/469, L225 28 July 1989

This limited the trade in live cattle to the EC to animals born after 18 July 1988, and demanded that none of them was the offspring of any cattle known to be suffering from BSE. The idea was that, as these exported cattle could not have been fed any BSE-infected material, if they did not catch it from their mother they could not be infected at all. At the time this seemed very reasonable. It was only in 1995, when the level of infectivity inside the herds was fully realised, that it became clear that this was in fact not so.

San Francisco

The Biology Department at the University of California in San Francisco was halfway up a multistorey block looking over the bay. I went to look for Dave Westaway, a molecular biology researcher in Stan Prusiner's lab, who had answered my letters from the other side of the Atlantic.

Scott from Edinburgh reported that scrapie inoculated into the eye travels along the optic nerve and is found in the areas of the brain to which the nerve goes.   *Alzheimer's Disease and Related Disorders*, 1989.

Haruguchi in San Francisco analysed the normal prion protein and the prions made out of them. He found that two small chains of sugar molecules were attached to the outside of the proteins. In fact he found many different forms of these sugar chains. Maybe this was the difference between different strains of scrapie.   *Archives of Biochemistry and Biophysics*, October 1989.

D.M. Taylor, of the MAFF Neuropathogenesis Unit at the University of Edinburgh, stated in a review on BSE and human health that by analogy with scrapie the risk to humans from BSE appeared to be slight. CJD was not common in shepherds, abattoir workers, butchers and so on who were exposed to excess scrapie, so why should they be at greater risk of BSE? Like all scientists of the time, he could give no answer on the degree of risk to humans.   *Veterinary Record*, October 1989.

'Prions are definitely the answer,' he affirmed over lunch. 'I just can't see how the groups in Yale and Edinburgh are going to continue with their position. Bolton destroyed everything in a sample of tissue and found that infectivity was still there. When he looked at the remaining soup of tissue he found that all that was left was a small group of proteins. When the proteins were purified they were found to be infective.'

> M.P. McKinley showed that if you inoculate hamsters with scrapie when they are only a few days old they had a shorter incubation period. In fact it seemed that if the infection took place before birth the incubation would be even shorter. This may mean that they are easier to infect when very young.   *Neurology*, October 1989.

'So how do you get around the fact that some strains of disease are different from others, and that the strain type is carried on from animal to animal as it's inoculated?' I asked. 'How can that be unless there's a factor associated with the agent that decides its strain type?'

> David Bolton from New York had set himself the target of analysing the prion protein. This was the protein that he felt was the cause of TSEs and was derived from the normal prion protein (PrP). So what alteration was made in PrP to turn it into a prion? So far he could find no protein structure change at all, but the molecule could not be completely deconstructed.   *Archives of Biochemistry and Biophysics*, 1987.

'I'm not really happy that these strain types are actually as perfect as they're putting across anyway. All I can say for the moment is that there must indeed be some method by which the protein retains its strain. But just because I don't understand it doesn't mean that it's not true.'

'Are you saying that BSE won't turn out to be the same as scrapie?'

'That's exactly what I'm saying. It will turn out to be the TSE associated with the prion protein of cattle. It will infect a different range of animals. It will produce disease in different parts of the brain of cattle and other species than in sheep. We've put the gene for the prion protein from a patient with Gersmann-Straussler-Scheinker syndrome [a human inherited form of TSE] into a mouse. The animal developed a spongiform encephalopathy spontaneously. What can they want, these scientists? In other words, all you need is the protein in its abnormal form being produced inside the cell. We didn't add any virus, we just added the GSS prion protein gene. So the disease is caused by a factor determined by that gene.'

'What about the scrapie disappearing from flocks exported to Australia, or reappearing in flocks restocked into areas of Iceland that had been emptied of sheep?' I asked. 'Where's the infection coming from there if it's not either in their genes already or appearing out of the blue?'

George Carlson in San Francisco showed that the scrapie prions in different mice were different and it was the difference in these that caused apparent 'strains' of scrapie with different properties, such as a longer or shorter incubation period. *Proceedings of the National Academy of Science*, October 1989.

This was directly against the findings in Edinburgh, where they had shown that genetically identical mice could become infected with different strains of scrapie. Clearly this was to be a battle.

'Scrapie's a hard nut to crack. It will probably turn out to be caused or partly caused by an environmental factor that depends on, or interacts with, the genes of the sheep.'

I decided that this was quite wrong and asked him where he got the idea. He handed me a copy of a book by Oppenheimer, *Scrapie: a Disease of Sheep*, which detailed 30 years' work by an excellent researcher who had died before he could finish writing up his findings.

I was taken around the lab and chatted to a number of young researchers. They explained the mathematics behind their work and the way various experiments were organised. Dave showed me the lab in which they extracted and purified the prion protein. The door was marked with a sign indicating the risk to workers who entered. We had to put on white coats and I could see that all the work was done behind the clear plastic frontages of fume cabinets. Air from the room was drawn into the cabinets through holes in the front, which enabled the researcher to put his or her arms through; the air flow pulled inwards, so that nothing from the cabinet got out and put anyone at risk in the room.

'I don't really see how you can assume that animal prions aren't a risk to humans,' said Dave. 'Humans might start to die because of work they did in a laboratory 20 years previously. It might be very difficult to demonstrate that a person dying of CJD had been exposed to an animal prion that long ago. We certainly shouldn't wait for proof, because it might be too difficult to produce. We should assume that prions are a risk and act on that assumption to protect the people in the lab. I don't know how many people have worked in the lab here, but Stan has more people here than in all the other labs together. I should think we'd be risking an epidemic of CJD if we didn't take adequate precautions.'

'So why are they telling us in the UK that BSE is just scrapie, and that as scrapie does not infect humans neither will BSE? All the work you're doing here is on scrapie in mice or hamsters, so surely there won't be any risk,' I said, expecting him to come out with a story about American insurance costs and medico-legal settlements in the courts.

> Jim Hope in Edinburgh has found scrapie associated fibrils — small, fine protein fibres — in the brains of cattle with BSE. They have to be concentrated and extracted out of the brain that is affected. They appear similar to those found in all other TSEs. *Nature*, November 1989.

It was reported in the *Veterinary Record* in March 1989 that Southwood had called for monitoring of BSE risk in vets. In other words he felt that vets might be at risk and should actually be monitored to see if they went on to develop a TSE.

'Well, I certainly wouldn't take a risk like that with myself. When the prion is passed from the sheep to another species it takes on the structure of the prion of the newly infected animal. Maybe it changes back if transferred back to the sheep, but in another species it's definitely different. We can even demonstrate the changes. There are statistics to show that when the animal that manufactures the prion changes it also changes the range of animals that it will subsequently infect.'

R.H. Kimberlin writes that scrapie is absorbed from the intestines easily if it is eaten, and then multiplies in the immune system inside the body.   *Virus Research*, December 1989.

'I must admit you certainly aren't taking any risks. The system you're using here looks like the way we handle possible tubercular samples in the lab, where one bacterium is enough to infect us,' I said. 'You do realise, don't you, that the group in Edinburgh claim the scrapie agent carries its own genes and so it doesn't change when crossing from one species to another?'

'Some of their work is brilliant, but they're going to find that the agent is nothing but prion protein and the apparently inherited factor comes from the genes of the infected animal and the structure of the prion. They will find that if there's no PrP gene in the animal then it can't become infected, and they will find that genetic mutations in the PrP will be all that's needed for the PrP to become a prion and infective.'

Dave Westaway was convinced; he had worked very hard on the subject. He handed me a book about 50 pages long – directions to be followed by all research scientists working on a TSE to avoid personal risk. I did not know then that the UK Advisory Committee on Dangerous Pathogens would produce a very similar book, admittedly five years into the future.

'In the UK we don't know which cattle are infected and which aren't. If we were to follow these directions with all suspect bovine tissue we'd be cooking our dinner inside a fume cabinet and wearing gloves to pick up a piece of liver,' I commented.

'Yes, the UK Government appears to be willing to take a risk with its population,' said Dave. 'While TB can be diagnosed and cured, of course, TSEs can't.'

£2,826,788 was paid to farmers in compensation for BSE in 1989.

We went over to the transgenic lab and watched someone trying to insert a specific gene into an ovum under a microscope. This was close to the animal house, where the hamsters and mice were looked after while they incubated their disease. The research team were always worried about contamination and about the possibility that their results could be looked on as invalid if any of their animals could be suspected of having caught the disease from some other source than the inoculum that they had given them.

'Are you suggesting that the animals might catch it from the food, or from the water, or from equipment, or other hamsters?'

'We have to worry about it, don't we? There are reports of mink, mice and goats apparently catching the disease from each other in a cage. People say there's such an enormous amount of infectivity in a single infected animal that we have to be wary of contamination. Samples or equipment just in the same fume cabinet or handled by the same hands may pass infectivity. Look at the figures — there might be 1000,000,000,000 times the amount needed to infect a hamster in a gram of hamster brain. Now surely that's infective stuff?'

No help from MAFF

The work on transgenic mice and hamsters was going ahead apace. The lab had already transferred the PrP gene of a patient with GSS to a mouse and found that the animal developed the disease several months later. The only odd thing was that many of the mice carrying the gene did not develop the disease, and there was no explanation for that at the time. They had also transferred the hamster PrP gene to a mouse and the mouse PrP gene to a hamster. What they found was that you could then infect the transgenic mouse with hamster scrapie very easily (whereas with a normal mouse it was relatively difficult) and infect the transgenic hamster with mouse scrapie (whereas with a normal hamster it was difficult). In other words the apparent specificity of the disease for the animal species depended on the PrP gene, and if the animal had a gene that permitted infection transfer was easy.

Bovine Spongiform Encephalopathy Compensation Order 1990 Statutory Instrument 222

By 1990 it was becoming clear that the number of cases of BSE was large enough to cause farmers considerable hardship. There was now evidence that the numbers reported in 1989 were below the actual figures. As a result compensation was increased from 50% of the value of the cow to 100%. This value was to be arranged between the MAFF veterinary officer and the farmer at the time of initial clinical diagnosis, and was to depend on the price of cattle at the time.

In 1990 prices were good. If all the farmer had to do was accept the money

---

60

> from the vet and let him take the animal away this must, apart from the stigma of having an infected herd, have been a good option. Even quite old cattle that had lost a lot of weight due to BSE would get a price from the vet that was reasonable for a standard animal at market. In a way it was almost bribery, but was a good method of finding out what was going on.

'Surely this must mean that the PrP gene is strongly associated with infection,' demanded Dave. 'It means that the disease depends on the gene. What more do they want to demonstrate that PrP is involved? Spontaneous disease, as in GSS, will happen with the right gene – and the species barrier of infection from another animal depends on the gene.'

'What about BSE?' I asked. 'Has anyone tried putting the human PrP gene into a mouse and seeing whether that made the mouse easier to infect with BSE?'

'As far as I know, no work has been done on BSE. OK, this is the biggest TSE that's ever been known. It's the biggest epidemic we can ever expect. But no BSE-infected tissue is available to us for research.'

'Just write to MAFF and ask for some!' I suggested.

> D. Serban showed that CJD could be diagnosed rapidly using antibodies to look for the prion protein. *Neurology, January 1990.*

'Do you really think we haven't tried? It's absolutely clear that your MAFF and our Department of Agriculture would much rather that all the research was done either by them or their direct allies.'

> A Food Safety Advisory Centre leaflet, picked up in a supermarket in January 1990, made the following statements. Beef is safe to eat. All BSE-infected cattle

are slaughtered and destroyed. In addition approximately 80% of cattle being slaughtered have not been fed meat and bone meal in their lifetime, the most likely cause of the disease. There will therefore be only a tiny proportion of animals incubating the disease. The BSE agent is concentrated in the specified offal of a cow. As a precautionary measure all these offals are now carefully removed from the animal after slaughter and are prohibited from entering the human food chain. Beef from cattle showing symptoms of BSE fed to or injected into mice does not produce the symptoms of spongiform encephalopathy, whereas infected offal does.

The Food Safety Advisory Centre was an organisation sponsored by major supermarket chains.

'Are you saying that they refused to give you any BSE-infected tissue?'

By January 1990, 5.1% of cattle herds in the UK had been affected with BSE. Most of these were in the south of England.

'Effectively, yes.'

'That's appalling, if you're the only people with a potential method for deciding whether people may be at risk from an epidemic. Surely, if the mouse's PrP gene is removed and a human one inserted, then the mouse would become infected by TSEs that would infect humans? You could then try infecting that mouse with BSE. If you succeeded, it would be good evidence that humans could be infected with BSE as well.'

'It wouldn't be that effective. We could only estimate that the risk *was* there – we couldn't say that BSE was *not* a risk to humans. In other words, if MAFF gave us tissue we could only come out with bad news for them, never good news,' he replied.

'What's good news or bad news for MAFF got to do with it? They're supposed to be acting on behalf of the UK population to ensure that food doesn't present any risk, not suppressing research so that meat sales are maintained.'

European Commission Decision 90/59, L41 7 February 1990

This limited from 1 March the export of live cattle from the UK to EC countries to those under six months of age intended for slaughter by six months – in effect, veal calves for feeding with a milky meal inside individual crates. The process is unhealthy and produces the white meat popular in France and The Netherlands. No calculations seemed to be available at this time on what percentage of the exported cattle would be infected, and no enforcement of the ban on specified offals for cattle under six months was suggested abroad.

The prevention by MAFF of wider research into BSE in San Francisco was so frustrating that eventually a research worker came over to the UK and picked up the head of a cow, presumed to be infected, that had been kept in a refrigerator for him by a farmer. He took it in a suitcase on the plane back to California. However, US Department of Health regulations demand that all imported food or animal products must have a licence, and this one certainly didn't. He was stopped at immigration and the head taken away. This may have been the act that finally made MAFF realise that they just were not going to be able to stop research into the subject, and would have to start making deals with the various research groups.

Andrew Forbes, President of the British Cattle Veterinary Association, announced that his group had asked for the prohibiting of interference in any way with BSE-infected cattle giving birth. 'The implications of this disease are too serious for salvage surgery to be considered a viable option.'

Veterinarians and BSE. Editorial in the *Veterinary Record* February 1990.

In the early days the impression had been given that MAFF was dragging its heels about giving information. In fact it was intensely active: 'a course must be steered between the Scylla of the too bland a view and the Charybdis of unjustified panic'.

MAFF had actually changed its advice concerning calving in infected cattle and had taken on the BVA's advice that this should never be assisted or by Caesarian section and now says that these should not be contemplated under any circumstances.

M. Cooke, official veterinary surgeon to Daventry District Council, offered specific guidance for vets handling BSE cases and referred to MAFF's directives. MAFF had suggested that to examine a cow for BSE it should be restrained. Mr Cooke felt that this was going to be difficult and that the animal might well kick out if it had BSE. He could not understand how MAFF could give directions for calving, cleansing and Caesarian sections for a cow with BSE. Why should it not be slaughtered immediately? MAFF's idea of protective clothing comprised the wearing of gloves and masks when the vet might be exposed to blood or fluid from a clinically sick animal. What about the ones that were not clinically ill? Should vets be wearing gloves for incineration and face masks continuously? *Veterinary Record,* March 1990.

It was now August 1989, and in July 1988 it had been announced that all BSE-infected cattle were the property of MAFF and that, if they were not reported to MAFF, the perpetrators would be committing a criminal act. All research work in the UK that is carried out on animals has to have permission from MAFF. If no certificate of permission is given and the research continues, this too is a criminal act. MAFF seemed quite able to prevent specific research from being carried out if it were inclined to do so.

In reply to a question in the House of Commons, Agriculture Minister John Gummer replied in these terms. Herds in which BSE had been confirmed: in England 69% of herds, in Wales 80.9% and in Scotland 88.1% of these, have had at least one case of BSE. Two cases have been recorded in 18.9% of herds in England, 11.8% in Wales and 7.9% in Scotland, while three or more cases have been seen in 18.1% in England, 7.3% in Wales and 4% in Scotland.

The annual incidence of BSE was then 0.2%, and 5.1% of all herds had been affected.

Up to the end of February 1990 £4,135,729 had been paid to farmers in compensation for BSE.

Oppenheimer and Scrapie

Oppenheimer's book brought up a few things of interest. Parry, author of the original edition, had tried for many years to breed sheep that would either be much more likely to develop scrapie or much less so. His problem was time: sheep generally developed the disease at about three years old, so each generation of breeding would take longer than that. In the end, however, he had shown that some breeds such as the Herdwick were much more likely, and some, for instance Scottish blackface sheep, much less likely to develop the disease, and that breeding did in fact make a difference. He claimed that he could see no apparent infection taking place. The epidemiology did not make sense for infection: how could a flock go for 20 years without a case, and then one appear, if there had been unaffected generations in between? Perhaps the infection could have come from the environment – in which case why weren't all the sheep in the flock or area affected in the same way? Perhaps the infection was particular to specific breeds of sheep – in which case, why did highly inbred populations of sheep not all get it in the same way? Perhaps, of course, it was not an infection at all and we were all kidding ourselves with a spurious piece of research in which the tissue of a case of scrapie, when inoculated, would transfer the disease to another sheep.

Experiments had been carried out by various workers who had put scrapie-infected sheep in pens with others to see whether the apparently uninfected ones became infected. No contact transfer of infection was seen. One experiment, when repeated using goats, indicated that they could 'catch' the disease from sheep; but no contact transfer to another sheep has been demonstrated. Parry was convinced that no infection was required, and that a 'poor penetration' gene was all that was needed to explain all the findings. This is a gene that is present in the chromosomes of many animals of a group but not used ('switched on') by every animal. The gene can only cause disease in the animals in which it is used, and as a result only a small proportion of the animals develop scrapie. I realised later that there was much more to this than was discussed by the published science of the day, and Parry's findings would have to be explained by any hypothesis of the agent that caused scrapie.

Dawson reported BSE being transmitted by injection from one cow to another
Veterinary Record, February 1990.

Safety first

The next day I arrived at the UCSF lab to give a talk about BSE in the UK, about its epidemiology and about how it appeared to be spreading. Some members of the audience felt that I was taking too stern a position and that a few cows, if their most infective tissues were removed, should not be presumed a risk to humans. But a German researcher was absolutely furious about the UK handling of the disease: when he got back home he was going to tell them the lot. At the end I offered everyone 'mad cow disease' ties. The brainchild of Dr Tim Ingles and Kevin Kerr in Leeds, they bore a picture of a dead cow surrounded by the words '*hodie mihi, cras tibi*' (me today, you tomorrow). They were seized with enthusiasm.

A *BMJ* editorial, headlined 'The safety of beef has not yet been tested and may not be testable', explained that BSE was fatal, untreatable, was passed from one species to another, was passed by mouth, was found in the tissues of asymptomatic animals, induced no immunity and might have a very long incubation period. Its author, Dr Matthews, the retired Professor of Clinical Neurology at Oxford, went on to say that we had been exposed to the equally mad sheep disease for a long time without evidence that it was infecting us. However, 'repeated claims that British beef is entirely safe to eat are very probably true and largely supported by the opinion of the Southwood committee: but such claims are scarcely scientific when the question has not been tested and is, perhaps, untestable.' *British Medical Journal*, February 1990.

In a laboratory it is easy to become blasé about the risk you are taking. Ian Pattison, a major researcher for MAFF who was emphatic that BSE should be assumed to be a risk to humans, told me of days in which he would be up to his armpits in sheep blood splatterings from animals that had scrapie. He realised, he said, that he had not died of scrapie and that scrapie was probably not a risk, 'but that was hardly the way to find out'. I had become blasé about some of the bacterial research I had been carrying out in the laboratory in Leeds, so when I saw the precautions taken against scrapie by the research team in San Francisco it gave me a bit of a jolt. At the lecture, I asked if anyone in the room (about 30 people) would be willing to eat UK beef sausages or feed them to their children. Nobody replied.

Molecular biology in Montana

Next day I flew to Montana to visit the Rocky Mountain Institute for the Study of Neurological disease in Hamilton.

Minor reported on an informal meeting on the significance of BSE for many biological and pharmaceutical products. It had taken place on 16 May 1988 at a private conference of pharmaceutical divisions of major companies. It was clear that no bovine product at all could be inoculated into humans. A product called surfactant, which is instilled into the lungs of babies to allow them to breathe more easily, was made from calves. This is just one product that was realised could no longer come from the UK. Information about this meeting became available to me in 1990.

Bruce Chesebro, who had worked on scrapie and the production of the prion protein by the PrP gene, and knew my standpoint on BSE, asked a relative newcomer there, Byron T. Caughey, to show me round the lab and organise the talk that I was to give the following day.

David Maclean, Junior Minister for Agriculture, admitted that five antelopes in British zoos had been confirmed as being affected by a spongiform encephalopathy. *Hansard*, 20 March 1989.

This was no minor research facility. The huge library contained all the available research literature, while the labs were crammed with equipment and split into many parts. Different sections were dedicated to different diseases, and it was clear that plenty of exciting research was going on.

Helen Grant, the (now retired) neuropathologist from Charing Cross Hospital, demands to know how Ray Bradley (the leader of the research group at the Central Veterinary Lab and an adviser to the Government) can possibly know that BSE is not going to turn out to be passed from cow to calf. If it is like scrapie in sheep, as the Government is always saying, then surely it will do as scrapie does and become endemic in the herd? *Veterinary Record*, March 1990.

Byron had a lot of ideas. At the time he was working with cultured nervous cancer (neuroblastoma) cells to see first if they could be infected with the scrapie agent, and then how the infection took place and the way it developed. Safety regulations here were as stringent as those I had observed in Prusiner's lab in San Francisco. Initially the team were not at all sure that infection could take place in the test tube, but eventually they managed to repeat experiments first carried out in Prusiner's lab and by Laura Manuelidis at Yale. The cells would produce the prions, but no sign of cellular damage could be seen.

'Look at the electrophoresis patterns that we produce from infected cellular cultures,' Byron said, pointing to a picture showing how the different proteins of the cells had been drawn apart by the passage of electricity through gel into which the extract from the cells had been inoculated. What you could see was a light band about halfway along the gel. This was PrP^{27-30}, produced when all the proteins were destroyed using a powerful enzyme called proteinase K, which would even destroy itself. The prion could not be destroyed completely, and the PrP^{27-30} was all that was left. 'So this is it? This is the infective agent? What about all the rest of the stuff that's left after the enzyme has had its go?' There isn't anything, is there?' I said, 'I thought that was part of Bolton's work, showing that when everything else was destroyed by proteinase K the infectivity remained.'

'No, look again, Steve. Look at the hole in the gel where I inoculated the fluid containing the proteins before separation. What's all that?'

Paul Brown in Washington found that scrapie brain infectivity continued even after autoclaving, or fixing in formaldehyde and it survived to a degree after being turned to ash at 360°C. *Journal of Infectious Disease,* March 1990. Now that is a very tough virus!

He was right, of course – there was plenty of other protein, it just had not been separated by the electrophoresis and had remained in the hole. In other words the particles were too big to pass into the gel.

'When they go around saying that there's got to be some DNA in the infective agent and how the electrophoresis-separated proteins don't remain infective, they're forgetting that there's plenty more left after the action of proteinase K.'

This was getting to be tough stuff for someone freshly thrown into heavyweight molecular biology. 'So what do you think it is?' I asked.

'It will be the same prion protein but in a poorly soluble form – the band of PrP^{27-30} is the bit of it that's become soluble. When they say that the extraction and purification procedures could leave plenty of things apart from prions to retain infectivity, they're right'.

'Does that mean the PrP^{Sc} [this is the name given to the type of PrP that has changed into the prion form] isn't the infective agent at all? Are you saying that many of the scientific conclusions made by Bolton and Prusiner are actually wrong?'

'As it happens, I think they're probably right – but

there's plenty of work yet before we can show it,' said Byron. 'Infected tissue can be chopped up and its protein separated into many different types or fractions by numerous methods. Whatever method we use, however, the fraction that contains the ability to infect another animal, i.e. the infective agent, always contains the PrP^{Sc}. Take the immunoseparation method, in which antibodies to PrP^{Sc} were used to extract from brain tissue only the protein that would attach to them. When this extract was inoculated into mice, the mice developed scrapie. If we took the brain of a mouse and destroyed as many of its proteins as we could with enzymes, what do we find? The only protein remaining was the PrP^{Sc}, and the infectivity wasn't destroyed either. If we took some brain extract and separated its proteins electrically, it just turned out that the fraction that contained the PrP^{Sc} also contained the infectivity. Come on, Steve, PrP^{Sc} is in this puzzle somewhere, surely?'

'I must admit it seems conclusive. But people have made the PrP artificially using bacterial culture methods, and purified it. When that's inoculated into a mouse, the mouse doesn't develop scrapie. Isn't that just as conclusive in the opposite direction – that there's more to it than just a piece of protein?' Maybe I was being too negative, but Byron didn't seem to mind.

'That's what we have to find out. How can a simple piece of protein cause an infection, and what is it about its structure that makes it infective? I'm trying some experiments to see how the protein is made and where it goes normally.'

He showed me more and more electrophoresis photos with images that were difficult for me to make out, and explained how he could inoculate a culture of infected cells with some radioactive labels that would join on to any proteins that were made. He could then follow what happened to the protein over the next few hours. When the PrP was looked for afterwards it was clear that it was being made continuously, and that in normal cells it was being deposited on to their surfaces. The protein was brought back into the cell between three and six hours later, and destroyed. When it re-entered infected cells, however, it was turned into PrP^{Sc} and seemed to be retained forever.

On 1 April 1989 BSE was made a notifiable disease throughout the EC.

Kitamoto in Japan found that under the microscope you could see if a mouse had died of CJD. If so, there would be 'kuru plaques' made of prion protein. The researchers decided that this was a better way to look for the disease than looking for spongiform encephalopathy, the normal procedure. Sometimes in an infected mouse there was no spongiform changes (little holes in the tissue where cells had died) present. *Laboratory Investigation*, April 1989.

The Stetsonville affair

Richard Marsh, a major expert on transmissible mink encephalopathy (TME), had come to work in the lab that Summer on a sort of sabbatical. He told me that whatever I did I must try to stop the UK Government from pulling the wool over people's eyes about BSE. Like so many others, he made it quite clear that BSE should be thought of as a fatal, untreatable disease of humans until there was evidence that it was not.

He had been involved in what was known as the Stetsonville affair. Apparently there had been an outbreak of TME on a local farm. When he and his colleagues arrived they discovered that the farmer had fed his mink on the tissues of a cow that had showed signs of a neurological disease, which sounded to Marsh very similar to BSE. Nothing of the cow was left to test, however, so it could only be recorded as an interesting find. For a long time people had felt that TME had come from scrapie in sheep in the same area. If you inoculate mink with scrapie, you get a similar disease in them – in fact mink were quite easy to infect. The only problem with this theory was that there was limited sheep farming in the areas where mink farming took place, and no epidemiological connection could be found. If, however, BSE rather than scrapie was the cause and BSE just appeared in rare spontaneous cases, you would expect rare cases of TME in entire mink farms, and that was exactly what happened. Maybe also, he suggested, this was the cause of the outbreak of BSE in the UK. Maybe 'in the beginning' there was a rare case of BSE which was fed to large numbers of other cattle in their meat and bone meal. Maybe it had nothing whatever to do with scrapie.

David Maclean, Junior Minister for Agriculture, admitted that £6,436,167 had been given in compensation for BSE by that time, and reported that the Southwood Committee had been predicting 350–400 cases per month to be found at this time whereas they were actually finding this number per week.   *Hansard*, 19 April 1989.

'Look, if scrapie caused BSE, why didn't these outbreaks appear all over the Western world? We have scrapie in America, and just because they get more grass and less meal here than in the UK wouldn't be enough to help us.' He went on, 'They are saying that the change in the way the meal was made in the early 1980s was the trigger which allowed scrapie to infect cattle. But even before that date 20% of the meal was made without using solvents, and, although they're telling you that scrapie has increased and so has the sheep population, it's simply not a big enough increase to make a difference in this type of disease.'

Mark Robinson in Washington State showed that although the infection of scrapie in an animal spread from tissue to tissue, it might actually change as it does so. He felt that the infectivity in the spleen and that in the brain were different in some way. *Journal of Infectious Disease*, April 1990.

This was important because it indicated that, if the prion was the infective agent, it must change in some way when progressing from one organ to another.

'You mean the change in infectivity level in the meal would have to be greater than that?' I asked.

'Yes, a fivefold change in the amount of scrapie in the feed might dubiously be enough to cause a huge outbreak. When we're working with TSEs we have to make changes in the order of hundreds of fold to alter things. Unless there was already almost enough to infect cattle anyway, nothing would have happened after such a minimal increase. If, however, it had been a rare case of BSE that appeared spontaneously (like here at Stetsonville) then there would no doubt be an outbreak. Once the brain of the BSE-infected cow got into the meal and was fed to another cow, that cow would get BSE.'

'Surely it could have just been a rare strain of scrapie, rather than a spontaneous case of BSE?'

'I suppose it could – or I suppose one cow could have become infected from a sheep and then infected the rest. But when you get to that position it no longer matters where it came from. Your people at MAFF are using the scrapie argument to prove that BSE won't infect humans. But if it was a rare strain of scrapie or if a certain type was able to infect the original cow then that argument falls flat.' Richard Marsh was quite determined that I should not let the Government get away with pseudo-science as a way of calming the population. 'If a BSE epidemic appeared in the USA, McDonald's could be decimated and the entire beef stock would stay uneaten.'

Dr David Clarke MP, Labour Front Bench Spokesman on Agriculture, asked Mr Gummer, the Agriculture Minister, for some statistics on the BSE epidemic.

Mr Gummer replied that the annual incidence for the year to 16 March 1990 was 0.2%, and that the number of cases seen had gone up in successive years.

1986	6
1987	413
1988	2235
1989	6420

The number per week was now around 350.   *Hansard*, 23 April 1990.

The huge beef lobby

While I was there, he suggested, why didn't I drive over the Rockies to see the group at Pullman? This was where the University of Washington State had its veterinary college and a research group were being sponsored by the USDA to carry out some research work into BSE. In other words the reason that Prusiner's lab had been prevented from importing BSE material to work on was nothing to do with stopping the disease entering the USA; it was because either MAFF or the USDA specifically did not want anyone else to have any.

In Pullman I was shown animals that had been inoculated with BSE, but no results were yet available (and certainly would not have been available to me anyway). It was clear, however, that the mink that had been inoculated with BSE developed a TSE which looked just like TME. A number had also been fed BSE. The researcher to whom I spoke expected that every species tested would end up infected. By analogy, he felt we should assume that humans would become infected with BSE.

The Bovine Animals (Identification, Marking and Breeding Records) Order 1990 Statutory Instrument 1867

This order stated that cattle born in the UK should be specifically marked and identified. The mother of any calf should be known and all these details should be recorded. This was largely because of EC insistence that only cattle from farms indicated to have had no BSE for two years could be exported to EC countries.

Initially the aim was that farmers could just record this information, which would be entered in a database on a central computer. When an exporter needed to know whether the calf he wanted to buy or export would be permitted in the EC, he would be able to consult the computer.

As far as I know this was worked at hard by a number of MAFF people, but the cost and difficulty of either getting information for the computer or supplying it to the various groups made the project ineffective. The information seems to have been of more use in computer analysis of bovine farming than in preventing infected cattle being exported.

It turned out that the USDA, the US Department of Agriculture, was very frightened of BSE and was absolutely determined that it should not become a risk in the USA. All the cattle imported from the UK since our outbreak of BSE had been collected up and either slaughtered or kept for observation on a small island off the east coast. None was permitted to become food for other cattle. It also seemed that the USDA had organised some research at the Centers for Disease Control at Atlanta in Georgia. I was not able to find out exactly what they were doing, but it probably involved looking out for imported cases of BSE.

The USDA was up to its eyeballs in research into BSE already, by the look of things, and I decided to visit the

Food and Drugs Administration people in Washington to ask what they were doing. I found that the FDA was run in a quasi-military manner, with many former army personnel walking around in uniform. It turned out that the FDA was involved in all food administration except beef, which was the province of the USDA. The reason seemed to be the difficulty in overseeing the production of such a complex product from an office; it had to be done by veterinary personnel on site.

It is difficult to describe just how big the beef lobby is in the USA: it is probably the next biggest after the gun lobby. Huge numbers of people have come to depend on beef as a source of income, and if BSE was to enter the USA all that would collapse. Sheep production in the USA was relatively low compared to the UK, and although scrapie was present it was not a huge economic problem. Originally scrapie-affected flocks had been slaughtered but it was found that that was ineffective at removing the problem, which just returned with the sheep that were used to restock. If a scrapie-type disease were to infect US cattle, and the US population found out, what would happen? That is something the USDA dare not contemplate; and whatever the cost of preventing or removing it, it would be worth the money.

The recognition by the scientific press that a realistic assessment of the risk to human health from BSE rather than a hollow 'beef is safe' as is heard from the Government would best counter public fears. Compared to nuclear power, another subject that the media has frantic scares over, BSE was almost an unknown quantity. To take the draconian 'Lacey' direction of mass slaughter seemed politically impossible, but even the minor suggestions concerning the ban on breeding from infected animals put forward by the veterinary groups had not been carried out. The author realised that Lacey's plan would cost the country several thousand million pounds, but there was always the fear that the reduced demand for beef would damage the farmers even more greatly.

> The editorial made it clear that we certainly did not know where BSE came from and, although scrapie was a nice idea, we certainly should not presume it. Nor could we state that maternal transmission from mother to calf or even adventitious infection did not take place. The juggling of some statistics could impress the population, but everything at the moment was hypothesis. 'Mad cows and the Minister', editorial in *Nature*, 24 May 1990.
>
> When I read this I was glad that someone in the scientific world was not just bowing to the word of MAFF, no matter how pseudo-science it might have been speaking. At least *Nature* was keeping its mind open to see the data.

That night after I had driven back from Pullman to Hamilton, Byron and his wife offered me a slab of beef, cooked over a barbecue at their home. Richard Marsh's wife was also there.

> The Central Veterinary Laboratory announced that it was examining a case of BSE in a cow born after the feed ban. It was believed to be a 15-month-old cow from southern England.
>
> The possibility that vertical transmission (from mother to calf) was taking place was a serious one and Peter Aldhous, the reporter concerned, had tried to find personal views. Many thought that BSE would be carrying on until the beginning of the next century anyway and that this was just a bad sign that it might go on further. Some were more worried and felt that vertical transmission was too much of a risk. They felt that a ban, currently unenforceable, that cattle with BSE should not be used for breeding should be demanded.
>
> Francis Anthony, chairman of the British Veterinary Association, thought that many countries all over Europe would have the disease and that the UK would be ahead of them. In the USA and France, however, it might be just dismissed as rabies. *Nature*, 24 May 1990.

'Do you think you're going to miss the beef when you get back to the UK?' Byron asked me.

'I think I'd miss this steak even if I was still eating British ones,' I said, and was told not to be such a creep. 'But I just don't know how to go about this in the UK. Everyone over here has told me that until we can definitely say there's no infectivity, to continue letting people eat UK cattle is sheer madness.'

> J.M. Wyatt in Bristol announced spongiform encephalopathy in a domestic cat. The media crowded around the vet's practice and got hold of the owner. The cat turned out to have been a Siamese determined to have its special food – steak, which it was fed regularly. *Veterinary Record*, May 1990.

'Well, muscle isn't really the most infective part of an animal,' he said, 'and you may well be able to eat that without worry.'

'There's a problem even there. We eat such a large amount of beef that even if there was only a small amount of infection per gram we'd still be getting quite a dose of disease in a meal,' I said. 'And anyway, for some reason they've permitted liver, kidneys, lungs, nerves, lymph nodes, bone marrow, eyeballs and so on to be eaten.'

Byron looked quite shocked by this.

'We know they happily throw anything that's not saleable as meat into sausages. And at the moment I'd have to assume that all UK beef sausages, beefburgers and meat pies contain unacceptable risk levels of BSE.'

I asked Mrs Marsh if she had read about the cat that had died of FSE (feline spongiform encephalopathy). The distribution of the disease in the brain of the cat appeared to be the same as that in cattle with BSE, not as in scrapie.

> R.G. Eddy, a vet, wrote to the *Veterinary Record* in May 1990 saying that he was sure he had seen cattle with BSE before the epidemic started in 1986. He thought he had seen

the disease at a rate of about one cow per 20,000 or 30,000 per year (much higher than the rate of CJD in humans). His position was important in that he was the first to put over the possibility that BSE might not have come from scrapie in the first place. But by this time the hysteria in the media was so great that the idea that BSE came from scrapie was being hung on to by MAFF; it was their main reason why BSE 'could not be a risk to humans'. Mr Eddy rather ruined MAFF's position, but his ideas have not been followed up.

'Surely if cats are starting to die and the humans are not, that must be a good sign,' said Mrs Marsh, who was probably fed up by now with hearing about TSEs, 'and the amount needed to infect a cat will probably be small anyway compared to the amount needed to infect a human, just because of our size.'

A.C. Palmer wrote to the *Veterinary Record* in May 1990 that he was not really surprised at the shortage of veterinary neurologists for BSE. It was simply because the Government had not funded their training, which had been asked for repeatedly.

'It's a pity,' I replied, 'but the incubation period appears to be more closely associated with the dose absorbed and the natural lifespan of the animal. So, as humans live seven times as long as cats, we might have to wait until way past the year 2000 before we see any cases in ourselves. Also, the size of animal may well have no significance for the amount needed for infection. It doesn't seem to matter in viral diseases generally.' It did indeed sound pretty grim, even to those of us who were used to the subject.

Agriculture Minister John Gummer wrote to Lady Wilcox of the National Consumer Council about BSE. He ended: 'Beef is safe. The precautionary measures taken go further than experts thought necessary to deal with any BSE risk, however remote and theoretical. Added to which, studies on scrapie show that the agent which causes the disease is not found in meat. British beef is therefore not a public health risk and can be eaten with complete confidence – a view endorsed by the European Community's top scientists.'

The letter was published in the press on 15 May 1990.

Across to the east

At Yale University in Connecticut I met Laura Manuelidis, who had been doing a lot of research into CJD and how it could be transferred from humans to many animal species. She was very interested in BSE: she knew that a risk to humans was possible and was just aching to get involved.

Francis Anthony, a British Veterinary Association spokesman on farm animals issues, dismissed as 'irresponsible' the claims by Leeds University Professor Richard Lacey that all cattle from BSE-infected herds should be slaughtered to protect human health. Mr Anthony said 'there was not a shred of evidence' that a human has caught an encephalopathy from an infected animal. *Veterinary Record*, May 1990.

'When I ask people their opinions about BSE, they all seem to say about the same,' I told her. 'They say they wouldn't eat UK beef products. Nobody seems to be arguing, and yet there seems to be such a battle going on between them.'

'In a subject that the world doesn't care much about, like scrapie or CJD, few scientific geniuses are going to be put on a pedestal by the media,' replied Laura. 'There's only going to be one winner, and they all want it to be them. So even if everyone agrees on almost everything, they must somehow find something to disagree about in order for them to win and not the other guy.'

'But surely when something like BSE comes along, and

lives may be lost, there may be many winners? At the moment it just makes it easier for the USDA over here and MAFF in the UK to find a scientist to agree with them if the scientific world appears to be spending its time infighting.'

'Well, it seems that way,' she said. 'I'm working on the viral cause of the disease. I've found that you can separate the infectivity from the PrP^{Sc} protein, and all I get is a deafening silence from my peers. I've been able to transfer CJD from one animal to another quite easily and found infectivity in the human blood. All I get is a quiet denial.'

'I suppose you could say they're being polite.'

'It would be a lot better if they repeated the experiments themselves and were then polite,' she said. 'Have they ever had a good look at the brain tissue of an infected animal under the electron microscope? If they do, they'll find the scrapie associated fibrils that may well be the viral particles or associated with them. Numerous other groups have actually found standard viral particles in the tissue.'

'Yes, but they don't all seem to find the same particles as each other, and those who repeat the experiments using other CJD-infected brains can't find them at all,' I said. 'It's only those fibrils, only the SAFs, which are always found in infected tissue even after a detergent extraction and precipitation procedure that seem to be so closely related to the disease. It's never found in normal tissue.'

'SAFs may well be there without the extraction procedure. It's just that they're of such unreliable shape and size that we can't always find them,' she said.

'Couldn't it be that you're *all* right? That the SAFs are the really infectious agent themselves but that they're made up of prion protein?' I suggested. 'Couldn't this explain why the infectivity can actually be filtered out using virus-size filters, and yet also why it's chemically so closely associated with the disease? It seems to me that the fact that it's not destroyed by the same processes that also don't destroy infectivity must be quite a coincidence.'

'So why is the distribution of PrP^{Sc} in a separation gel not exactly the same as the distribution of infectivity?' She was talking about a recently published piece of work from her lab, in which they had taken an infected brain and tried to separate the proteins from each other electrically. They then tested the different fractions and found that, yes, the fraction in which the PrP^{Sc} was found did indeed carry infectivity – but so did all the other fractions, and they carried more!

I acknowledged the problem. Nevertheless, a number of answers had been put forward.

Next I talked to a German scientist who had been carrying out some research with Laura. He was adamant that BSE was quite horrifying and said he would tell everyone he knew who visited the UK never to eat any beef products.

'Do you include muscle as a dangerous food?' I asked.

'Of course I do. We've already shown hamster flesh to contain infection, and you must know that mink muscle and goat muscle have been shown to contain infection as well. I think it would be stupid to assume that BSE is not present in bovine muscle.'

'Don't forget that no infection has been found in the muscle of sheep or mice,' I reminded him.

'Yes, but the test on sheep was done by inoculating the muscle into a tiny mouse, which meant that only 3mg could be injected. And bearing in mind the species barrier, I can't think that this rules out infectivity actually being found there. It just shows that they don't know how to test for it in a sufficiently sensitive way. As for the mouse muscle, I expect the amounts that were inoculated were simply too small to contain enough infection.'

'So you're saying that the only experiments that would have been sensitive enough to look for the relatively low amounts of infectivity in meat were the ones in the goat, the mink and your hamsters?' I asked.

'Schools ban beef in meals': headline in London *Evening Standard*, 15 May 1990.

'Yes. That's exactly what I am saying. What are the advisers to MAFF thinking of? Why are they not telling MAFF this themselves?'

I went back into Laura's office. She expressed the same surprise that UK scientists were keeping their heads down and not complaining to the Government.

In mid-1990 Germany banned UK beef, followed by the French banning the import of all UK beef, live or dead. This represented an annual loss of £183 million to UK exports. They were followed by Italy and then Switzerland.

'Maybe they are,' I said. 'The meetings of the Spongiform Encephalopathy Advisory Committee are held in private and only specific people are invited to give evidence. The information that the committee receives is organised by MAFF, and abstracts of everything are put forward to the committee members. They couldn't really read all the data themselves because there's too much of it. I get the impression that the Government feel that, should BSE become a disaster for tourism to the UK, cause the destruction of the UK beef industry and suggest that children were being fed potentially fatal foods at school, then it would reflect on them politically. In fact the error was made by theoretically non-political people who felt they were changing the way in which beef meal was made for good economic reasons.'

The Movement of Animals (Amendment) Order 1990 Statutory Instrument 1868

It was becoming clear that cattle were moved around the country regularly and it was difficult to find out exactly how this took place. It was now possible, given the long incubation period of BSE, that livestock would need to be traced several years in arrears. The period for which farmers had to retain their movement records for cattle was therefore extended to 10 years.

The natural life expectancy of a cow is 28 years but they are generally slaughtered by the age of 10 and most of them are killed before they are five. This order was made probably because MAFF could see that the disease had started long before it was first reported in 1986; because if they were to carry out efficient epidemiological work, they would need to know about cattle transfer; and because BSE was going to go on for some time, with some cattle dying after the age of 10.

'What should your Government have done?' asked Laura.

'They should have admitted that an error had been made (not by them), and that it was going to cause severe damage to the beef industry. They should then have applied for money through the European Economic Community, which has an enormous agriculture budget, to limit the damage to UK farmers.'

Agriculture Minister John Gummer was shuffled backwards and forwards across the Channel trying to remove the laws that the various countries had put in place against UK beef. In the end he was successful, but they did demand that Britain would not export any bone-in meat to the EC from farms where BSE had been found. This package was announced to the House of Commons on 7 June 1990.

It was time to get down to brass tacks again. I was here for a purpose. 'Would you mind answering some specifically technical questions about your work?' I asked.

'Go ahead. Everything we've done here is repeatable.'

'You're the person who says that the agent of a TSE is a classic virus. Could I ask you to explain to me again how you continue to maintain that position while so much information is coming from California about prions?'

'There appear to be strains of scrapie. In other words the agent carries something to indicate the disease type. There's no indication of how this can be done with just a piece of protein. People have actually found virus-like particles in the brain of infected animals. When they carried out the experiments to destroy the agent, they simply didn't do them well enough. It would only need one virus to remain for the stuff to remain infective. Also, we've shown that when you separate the proteins from the extractions the infectivity isn't necessarily found in the same fractions as the prion protein. While the protein and infectivity can be separated from each other, I don't think that this prion can be claimed as the agent.'

European Commission Decision 90/261, L146 8 June 1990

The French and Germans made it clear that they simply did not believe the information being given to them from the UK that exporters were following the rules to the letter. They felt that infected cattle were being exported and put a ban on the import of all UK beef.

Mr Gummer was horrified that these countries should do such a thing to a food that he would feed to his daughter without any feeling of risk (we must remember that Gummer's information came from MAFF). EC agreements eventually restored the trade in beef but demanded that the UK database [see p.76] would be used to assist checking of export certification.

At the time it was not clear how this would work, as inadequate information was present on the database of MAFF and there were inadequate numbers of people to staff the supply of such enormous amounts of data to exporters. There was no information reaching the press of an exporter checking the cattle he was taking out

86

> of the country, finding one or two to be from infected herds, and taking them back for a refund. At the time it was felt that this would be difficult and expensive to enforce.

'What about the fact that the effect of infectivity isn't stopped by treating tissue with enzymes that break up DNA or RNA? What about the inability of X-rays or ionising radiation to destroy infectivity? How could either of those be true if nucleic acid was present?' I could see that she had heard these arguments a hundred times.

'Enzymes can only break up DNA and so forth if they can get at it. If the nucleic acid is protected the enzymes won't destroy it, by whatever means. Look, there was some perfectly good work published in *Nature* recently showing that the scrapie agent could be destroyed by heat in a similar manner to other viruses. Don't believe all you hear. Everyone wants to be the big cheese, but it doesn't necessarily mean they're right.'

My next port of call, via the Staten Island ferry, was a research institute which looked into neurodegenerative diseases. My guide was to be Thomas Borage, a short-term researcher in the department which was working on the distribution of the infective agent of the disease inside the brain.

> 'Fears over mad-cow bodies on village tip.' These were reported in a Yorkshire newspaper, the *Keighley News*, on 8 June 1990. The banned offal was taken from Keighley abattoir to the tip at Cross Roads because this was a 'toxic waste' site. At the time the number of cattle requiring to be incinerated and the amount of offal that had to be disposed of were growing rapidly. New incineration plants were being built rapidly but could not yet cope. There were fears that underground streams could carry the infective agent back to the fields on which the cattle were grazing but the tip's manager, Tony Robertshaw, was more worried about rats, foxes and seagulls just picking off the pieces that they wanted and passing the agent out in their faeces elsewhere.

He showed me some pictures of brain sections that he had stained with immunogold – minute round gold nuggets. When added to the surface of the section to be stained they would attach themselves to the antigen or antibodies. Under the electron microscope you could therefore see where the antigen was. The nuggets were so small that a thousand of them might fit across the width of a cell. He pointed out the crystal-like objects that were becoming attached to the gold. They seemed to be inside the cell as well as outside, and could even be seen crossing the membranes. Presumably the crystalloids were the scrapie associated fibrils found after extraction procedures. At that time there was great argument as to whether they were actually present in the real tissue rather than a result of the extraction. Harash Narang had demonstrated the same thing and been effectively ignored by MAFF. These photographs were stunningly clear and really not open to argument.

> Narang in Newcastle found that by using a simple method of electron microscopy it was possible to diagnose CJD. This was an important find: it meant that cattle could be diagnosed before their tissues are sold. *Lancet*, March 1990.

I asked him if he knew about the work being done in Atlanta.

'I just don't know,' he replied. 'The information on this sort of thing just does not get around, on the whole. It's the politics. By rights we should be warning all the people visiting your country not to eat any UK beef products. Can you imagine how that would go down for UK–US relations? I know that a number of meetings have taken place between the USDA and MAFF on the subject. They called in Gajdusek's boys to be the advisers.'

> Goldfarb in Washington found that patients with CJD or kuru consistently lacked any mutations in their prion protein gene. In other words they were either infected from outside or perhaps a single cell became mutated somewhere in the body. *Experimental Neurology*, June 1990.

This was not really a surprise: Gajdusek was the Nobel Prize winner who worked at the National Institute of Health in Bethesda, just down the road from Capitol Hill.

'So what came out of that?' I enquired.

'Well, I got some work. Maybe that's a good thing. I'm going to be moved from here to work with the guy from Plum Island where all the UK-imported cattle are quarantined. Worry's not the word for BSE at the moment – it's fear. You must have noticed that the US Government has made virtually no statement on BSE. Ask Gajdusek what's going on – maybe he'll be more enlightening. As far as I can see they just aren't telling anyone what is happening. Just don't ask them to eat any UK beef.'

'Would you eat any?'

'I really don't think I would. But don't take this as an insult or anything. And I'm not exactly one of the big fish in this question.'

> Goldfarb in Washington found that various unrelated patients with CJD had the same mutation in the gene that coded for their prion protein. *Experimental Neurology*, June 1990.

After that I went to see Dr Merz, who had published a number of basic science papers on scrapie. She was quite adamant that the risk of BSE should be avoided at all costs and asked me what the UK was going to do about it. Among other things, I told her that Richard Kimberlin had advised the UK Government that the removal of specific offals would be adequate to avoid any human risk.

'How does he know?' she asked.

> John Collinge from St Mary's Hospital in London reported that they could now identify patients with an inherited disease associated with prions, without their brain needing to have the characteristic appearance under the microscope. This was done by looking for changes in the genes that were associated with the illness, using a new technique called the polymerase chain reaction (PCR), by which it was possible to multiply millions of times a single gene so that there was enough to analyse. *Lancet*, July 1990.

'Well, he doesn't, but he's assuming that BSE is like the other TSEs and he feels that the same action would be adequate for them.'

'That's what you get, I suppose, when you assume that they have their own genes. He must realise that the BSE agent is at least partly made using the genetic plans of a cow and scrapie from the genetic plans of a sheep, no matter where they came from originally. How was he picked to advise them?'

> In July 1990 Tony Lees from Powys wrote to the *New Scientist* trying to bring to the attention of farmers the risk of BSE being passed from one cow to another by giving injections to many cattle with the same needle, a common practice.

'The Government would have picked him. I expect it would have been MAFF themselves,' I replied.

'Kimberlin's a clever man, but he isn't the only one involved in the subject and for something quite as frightening as this the UK Government really should have listened to some more opinions.'

'I think they talked to Gajdusek,' I said.

Goldfarb in Washington showed that particular changes in the gene for the prion protein were associated with a familial form of CJD. About 10% of CJD appears to have been inherited in some way and his work showed that this might be due to a particular mutation. Indeed, the same mutation was found in a number of families with CJD that appeared to be unrelated. *Lancet*, July 1990.

In 1990 Larry Thompson explained in the *Washington Post* the fear concerning BSE. Imports of cattle to the USA had been banned. When asked, Gibbs at the National Institute of Health in Washington said that BSE was just scrapie disease, which had been with us for two hundred years without casuing a problem. Gary Cowman, associate director of science and technology with the National Cattlemen's Association, said that the disease, if it came to the USA, would be 'a catastrophe, economically'. The real threat, he said, would be consumer perception. In Britain at this time a thousand schools had dropped home-produced meat from their menus, and that was seen by the American farmers as frightening.

'Just don't worry about it'

Gajdusek's group worked at the National Institute of Health in Washington. I was introduced to a Dr Gibbs, who told me, 'Just don't worry about it. BSE is a problem. We all know it's a problem. But let's not get screwed up about it.'

I suspected he had been warned about me and had decided to infer that I was being neurotic. Fortunately two of his researchers followed me outside and clearly felt differently.

'People are punch-drunk with food scares,' said David Lewis, a spokesman for the UK Meat and Livestock Commission. 'Next we'll see killer cabbages.' The MLC had spent approximately £200,000 on an advertising campaign to counteract the 'inaccuracies, speculation and misguided statements' of the media concerning BSE. That came on top of a £4 million print and television campaign to tout red-meat consumption, plus a £16 million research programme to investigate the causes and transmission of BSE. *US News and World Report*, July 1990.

'He's a determined man, but that doesn't mean he's right,' one said. 'I certainly wouldn't even touch an infected cow's liver in the UK.'

'We do the experiments with this sort of illness in fume cabinets and wearing plastic gloves. We certainly don't eat any!' said the other.

'Keep going. Don't let them stop you. Remember that they have a lot of power. This is heavy research and we simply don't know enough. Gaj has done a lot of the stuff here and found that Stan Prusiner is almost certainly correct with his ideas about the prion.'

Dealler and Lacey calculated the risk to humans from beef by working out the number of infected animals that we would be eating and the amounts of infected tissue that were eaten from each one. The numbers were inaccurate, but showed that the risk to humans was certainly not 'nil' as had been claimed by MAFF officials. They showed that TSE infectivity appeared in the tissues long before symptoms appeared and were found in almost all the tissues of the body if adequately sensitive techniques were used. They showed that the range of infectivity expected in the bovine tissues eaten overlapped with the range needed for a TSE to infect another animal by mouth. *Food Microbiology*, July 1990.

We were absolutely inundated with reporters after this and I kept my head well down. Lacey, not afraid of the cameras and willing to tell people of the risks involved, was on a dozen TV programmes. We were expecting to see his head on a pole outside the lab one day. As it happened, the farmers who got in touch with him were generally polite and worried rather than aggressive. They actually wanted to know what was going on and did not necessarily believe MAFF.

'We separated that protein to as high a purity that we could, and found it was infective when inoculated into animals.'

'So why does Gajdusek continue to call the infective agent a virus?' I asked.

It appears that CJD is more common than is reported in the UK. Roberts' work at St Mary's Hospital in London suggested that 1500 cases would appear in the UK and not 50 as reported. The difference is because many dementia patients are never subjected to a post mortem. It may well be that the actual number of cases of prion disease is some 250 times greater than is considered currently. *Lancet* editorial, July 1990.

'The politics of this science are so tight that I can't explain what happens. Some of them just hate Stan for finding it out and being right. If they'd found it, they'd be hated instead. The jealousy is shocking. I'm just glad I'm at the bottom.'

UK government vets

So Dave Westaway and the crew in San Francisco were quite determined that prions were the answer. Laura Manuelidis was sure in her mind that a virus was in there somewhere, and we shouldn't abandon a known infective agent for one that might make someone famous until there was enough evidence. Everyone except Gibbs at NIH seemed to be concerned about BSE. It is, of course, difficult to be sure that they were not saying that because I was a visitor from across the Atlantic and they felt they had to be polite to me. I doubt this, however. After listening to Richard Marsh and his direct worry about the human risk, I was quite certain that American researchers were not in the 'sit on your hands with your fingers crossed' category that seemed to characterise a number of the ones in the UK.

Howard in London carried out a survey at the Maudsley (acute psychiatric) Hospital, asking if the doctors had changed their attitudes to eating beef.

- 65% of responders said 'yes' and put this down to concerns about BSE
- 52% said they now ate significantly less beef

This was taken as an indication that reassurances by the Chief Medical Officer were not regarded as valid by his medical colleagues. *Lancet*, August 1990.

I flew back to Heathrow and next day went to see John Wilesmith at the Central Veterinary Laboratory at Weybridge in Surrey. CVL, like many UK government establishments, looks as if it has never had enough money at any time. John's office was on the ground floor of a small building that looked as if it desperately needed some improvements – very different from what I had found in the USA. I don't think we appreciate the work done by many civil servants and the fact that they are often poorly funded. John was in charge of the epidemiological work on BSE, but was also having to raise statistics on many other diseases as well. I asked him to explain the current BSE situation in the UK.

'The numbers of cases are still going up rapidly and there doesn't appear to be a predictable peak at the moment. We seem to have fed so many cattle with the infective material that the number that end up with it could be very high. It certainly seems that the disease is everywhere in the UK, to a small degree in the Republic of Ireland, but nowhere else unless we've exported it to them.'

Bovine Spongiform Encephalopathy (No. 2) (Amendment Order 1990 Statutory Instrument 1930

In September 1990 the ban on the use of suspected bovine offals as food for other animals apart from ruminants was extended to all animals including poultry.

This came directly after the report that a pig had died of a spongiform encephalopathy after a large inoculation. The incubation period was probably too long for it to appear as a disease in all but a minute fraction of pigs, which are mostly slaughtered within a few months of birth. Chickens also do not live long enough in modern farms for the disease to be a risk. The problem that BSE may indeed be infecting the animals but not in high enough quantities to show up was not considered. The bodies of animals have not been shown to excrete TSEs and so, if a pig eats some BSE and we eat the pig, are we eating the BSE that remains in the animal's tissues? No research has been done into this.

MAFF seemed fed up at having to carry out an action against what they saw as a hypothetical risk. Continual pressure was needed to goad MAFF into action, despite the possible effects if no action were taken.

This order also fulfilled the EC demands and prohibited export of the offals to the EC.

'At the moment the NPU in Edinburgh is the biggest place for TSE research in the whole of Europe and they say they've had minimal extra funding since BSE has appeared. They say their research is decided by here and they are virtually being sent directions. It must be incredibly frustrating for a group like that when a new disease, never known in the world before, appears to sit and watch while CVL takes over.'

Richard Lacey was determined to make it clear that there were more risks from beef concerning BSE than MAFF would have us think. Muscle could be contaminated with BSE in three ways: from the nerves inside it, from the lymphatics inside it and because a cow carcass is often cut up with saws. These may go down the length of the spine and straight through the spinal cord, splattering infective material over abattoir workers and the rest of the meat. Washing does not remove it properly.   *Yorkshire Medicine*, autumn 1990.

'The politics of this are rife. We've fought for funding and for research to get going, but politicians don't act as fast as scientists,' he said.

'What do you think about these reports from Harash Narang that there may be a method of diagnosis of BSE using electron microscopy and a brain biopsy?'

'Attempts were made to repeat his tests. All I can say is that the results were not as expected,' he said. 'At the moment all we can do is to take the histology result as being the true result.'

'Is nobody trying out immunological staining of the tissue to look for PrP?'

'I really don't know everything that is going on everywhere. My bit is the epidemiology, and it's difficult enough.'

'How do you feel about the results in the zoo animals?' I asked, trying not to be too aggressive. 'Are we seeing large numbers?'

'No. One here, two there. As a proportion of the herd they are, however. Presumably kudu are extremely sensitive to the disease.'

'That must seem a bit odd. Surely if the disease is coming from cattle we would expect cattle to be most sensitive to it and other animals, whatever they were, to be less sensitive.'

'First case of BSE in victim's offspring.' The calf of a kudu developed a spongiform encephalopathy (SE) at London Zoo, its mother had died of SE, and they did not think that it had been fed any infective food. *The Independent*, 14 December 1990.

'I can't change the figures. There really does seem to be a relatively high percentage going down with it in the kudu herd at London Zoo. We just have to find out why.'

David Maclean, the Junior Minister for Agriculture, said that in November 1989 random ante-mortem inspections of cattle submitted for slaughter at non-EC-approved abattoirs were commenced. He claimed that Ministry vets carried out regular monitoring at markets.

It was only later that we were to question just how much inspection this represented, and whether adequate attempts were being made to find cases of BSE.

At that point we heard footsteps approaching. A man entered the room.

'Good to meet you, Dr Dealler. I'm Ray Bradley. I hope John has been telling you about all the good news that is appearing concerning BSE.'

'Is there good news?'

Wilesmith of CVL demonstrated that there was a good chance that the BSE epidemic might be associated with the change in the way that renderers produced meat and bone meal (MBM). For many years about 70% of the factories had used benzene, petroleum spirit, hexane or perchlorethylene to dissolve out the fat from the meat. In about 1977 this process changed over to the use of heating, centrifugation and then pressing of the tissue. These processes varied around the country, but 90% changed over to the centrifugation method. He felt that the new process would have left more fat in the MBM, which might have protected any scrapie agent from the effect of heat, and that the formed hydrocarbon solvent might well have damaged the agent itself.

Wilesmith made it plain that the epidemiology was not consistent with a hypothesis involving the emergence in the sheep population of a novel strain of scrapie which is pathogenic for cattle. Rather, the data was consistent with the hypothesis that the occurrence of BSE was the result of an increase in exposure to the scrapie agent.

However, he did agree that the findings were also consistent with a cattle-adapted strain of scrapie, which had been in the bovine population for some time. *Veterinary Record,* March 1991.

It was interesting that the parts of the country where most of the MBM was produced were not the places where BSE had seemed to rise quickly.

'It appears that the disease will be stopped by the change in cattle-feeding methods. We've introduced a change in the abattoir processes to prevent any infective material reaching humans. Surely that must be good news?'

'But you were forced to introduce those changes by the UK scientists. MAFF wouldn't have taken them, and we'd still be eating frighteningly risky tissues if they hadn't. Anyway, the offal ban doesn't take effect until November and should have been enforced immediately. I can't think of any reason why, if something is agreed to be a danger to human life, action against it should be put off for five months.'

'There was only a minor risk to humans anyway. I don't understand the problem.'

'What!' I suddenly got very angry, which is rare for me. 'Cattle incubating a fatal disease, for which there's no treatment and no method of diagnosis, and which is known to be transmitted by mouth from one animal species to another, are entering the human food supply – and you can't see there's a problem?'

'Scrapie didn't infect us for 250 years, so why should we worry about BSE?'

This man did not seem to understand either medical ethics or TSEs. Either that, or I didn't. And he was in charge of the Department at CVL that was advising the Government.

Farmers sold cattle with signs of disease to intermediate farms, presumably to avoid the social stigma and a drop in the values of their herds.

The chance that farmers could get more money for a sick cow from MAFF veterinary officers than they would from the market made them good things to sell to anyone happy to take them.

A number of farms, including one near Ilkley in Yorkshire and one near Chester, would buy in cattle and have them taken away by the VOs. The original farm from which the cow had come would not have to admit to any cases of BSE when other cattle were taken to market, and the farmer would therefore get more money for them.

CHAPTER FOUR

Giving evidence at Westminster

Professor Lacey had offered to go down to London to give evidence on BSE to the House of Commons Agriculture Committee in June 1990, and in just a few days we had put together a report as the basis for a memorandum answering the questions in advance. Although the committee came from various political parties, eleven were farmers and the twelfth a butcher. The Professor's previous pronouncements to the press and on television had forewarned them about his opinion on the subject, and we thought he might be in for a rough ride.

I also knew that the subject was so complex for a non-scientist that they probably wouldn't know the right questions to ask. I was going to be sitting in the room with the press and felt I should bring with me the scientific details that made it clear that BSE, like other TSEs, should be thought of as a danger until proven otherwise. This wad of papers sat in my shabby bag as we queued to get into the conference room. Also waiting to give their views were three neuropathologists: Helen Grant, formerly of Charing Cross Hospital, Ivor Mills from Cambridge and Dr Roberts from St Mary's Hospital in London. All were determined that humans should not be put at risk from BSE.

When Lacey was called to answer questions he walked up with an air of confidence and sat down before the committee. But the questions asked seemed to be of minor significance – mostly about whether he had enough knowledge of the subject or whether he should speak about things that were really somebody else's province.

Lacey, determined not to be put down, continued with his aim of putting information to the committee. We did not know if BSE would be infective to humans and we did not know if it would not be so. As it was a fatal disease with no method of treatment, the Government should err on the side of caution and not take a risk with the public. The chairman, Gerry Wiggin, was determined to hear what risks Lacey felt were possible in the short and longer term. Lacey told him directly that this sort of disease could become a major cause of death in Britain, and said we should take action to prevent such a calamity. Wiggin made it clear that he felt that scare stories got nobody anywhere. As I had feared, the committee did not know enough to ask the right questions of Lacey anyway. They did not appear to know that there was no method of testing anything for the presence of infection without actually inoculating it into the brain of a cow. They did not seem to realise that animals inherently lacked any way of forming immunity to the agents of TSEs, nor that the disease could not be destroyed by cooking.

A triumph of non-communication

After about half an hour of listening in frustration I decided to leave with my bag of scientific papers and try some other direction. The Ministry of Agriculture was not far away. Some of the questions asked seemed so simplistic that I felt the people in MAFF, who would, with the Department of Health, have to produce a document at the end, would have nothing to go on.

'Could I please talk to someone involved with BSE or the handling of the current Commons committee?' I enquired of the uniformed doorman who let me in. He said he would telephone and ask.

'I'm afraid nobody is willing to see you,' came the eventual reply.

'Rubbish. Do you think I could talk to them directly, please?' After listening to the committee I had to keep calm. 'If there's anyone here who's involved with the committee I'd probably be of use to him.'

'I'm afraid we cannot do that.'

'In that case, could you let the person who doesn't want to speak to me know that I have some information that I feel his department should have concerning the infectivity of animal tissues.'

'That's fine, sir. I'll take it from you here.'

'Unfortunately it will need explaining – it's rather complex'. He telephoned the man again. He offered to send down his secretary.

'This is really rather rude. Does he do this often?'

'We can't let anyone in, sir. It's because of all the risks.'

'In that case could I speak to his secretary?'

He telephoned again and said that she would come down to pick up the papers. A young woman came down and asked me for the papers to take away. I told her that they really needed to be explained because they were heavy science. She rang upstairs again.

'Could you just leave them here with me?'

I then spent half an hour sitting on a chair in the corridor writing information tags to be clipped on to the papers. There were about 23 that I thought they should definitely have. All were carefully ordered and then given to her. I asked for them to be returned to me in due course. The scientific papers came back to me about a month later in exactly the same order (although two were missing), as if otherwise untouched. For a government department called the Ministry of Agriculture, Fisheries and *Food* this was not impressive. Information continued to be released suggesting that various animal tissues did not become infective whereas the scientific papers made it clear that this was not valid.

102

The outcome: the committee's report

On various days at the committee the different witnesses had answered specific questions that Lacey had raised with the media. Southwood was asked how he knew that the disease would be a 'dead end host'. He said that American work had suggested that the more species a TSE went through the more difficult it became to infect and, as they must assume it came from scrapie, BSE would therefore go no further. The committee did not like that, and pointed out the various other species that had since become infected with BSE.

The final report, put together by the civil servants involved, was actually quite good. But it shared something with the Southwood Report. In the same way they assumed that BSE was derived from scrapie and, if scrapie does not infect humans, what's the worry anyway?

They felt that BSE probably did not contract through contact, and that food was probably the only route. They admitted that not enough information was available to rule out vertical transmission from mother to calf; but even if it was, they said, it is unlikely that every one of the offspring would become infected and so the numbers would gradually fall anyway over the following generations. Wilesmith had been their one ray of light, showing that vertical and horizontal transmission were unlikely. They recommended that the Department of Health make an annual report on the incidence of CJD.

They were, however, taken in by the lack of transmission of scrapie from sheep muscle to another kind of animal. They did not seem to see that when scrapie was inoculated into a mouse only a minute quantity was involved. They also did not seem to grasp that humans ate relatively large quantities of food – large enough to get past such an inefficient route of transmission.

Nor did they seem to realise that the regulations about

not including various offals in human food were not watertight. The reports from local authority environmental health officers that the committee read showed how difficult it was to implement the legislation.

They asked many scientists whether or not BSE was a risk to humans. These people generally shrank from giving strict reassurances and the committee took this as just meaning that, like all things, BSE cannot be certain. Unfortunately the committee did not seem to understand that many of the scientists did think BSE to be a risk, but felt under pressure not to say so. The committee probably heard what it wanted to hear. It felt that the measures taken by the Government concerning the banning of beef offal should 'reassure the people that eating beef is safe'.

They criticised the Government's slow implementing of an offals ban, especially in Scotland. Various organisations had been left behind, including the Institute of Environmental Health Officers which did not have sight of the regulations until two weeks after they came in.

The committee also attacked the severe delay, seven months in all, between the submission of the Tyrrell Report and its publication (a similar thing as had happened with the Southwood Report), so that arrangements had been made for its implementation before the House of Commons ever saw it. This was felt to be indefensible, and it is not really surprising that many MPs felt that the Government was simply making the rules and carrying them out without referring them to Parliament. They made this clear in demanding that the Minister go beyond the scientific lines of advice to make the population feel better about their food.

They recommended various changes in the abattoir procedures. For instance, splitting of the skull should be outlawed. It was also suggested that vertical cutting of the spine, which tended to include the spinal cord, should be stopped as fragments of the cord would affect the abattoir worker carrying out the procedure.

They asked that MAFF introduce a computerised system for tracking and logging cattle so that it would be possible to know if herds were becoming infected. The committee was very indignant that MAFF had not done this already. Now there were no excuses.

They demanded a statutory ban on the inclusion of offals in any pet food or in the feed given to pigs and chickens. At the time this was being carried out voluntarily. Indeed they demanded that the ban on bovine offals should be extended to include cattle under six months old. The worry about the beef industry was acute. Only recently had the Government introduced 100% compensation to farmers for cattle with BSE. The rendering industry, which took 1.75 million tonnes of animal waste every year was having to charge the abattoirs for taking away the offal and carcass remains. They were worried that foreign importers might start to find British beef too expensive.

Some things that they suggested were clearly difficult to carry out and police: the stopping of breeding from cattle with BSE, for instance, and the maintenance of the offal ban in slaughterhouses. They did not, however, demand random testing of cattle for BSE, shop labelling of meat that had come from infected herds, warning signs, information packages, specific research projects to assess human risk, and many other aspects that were considered relevant to human health. The committee's original worry had been the damage that the media 'scare stories' were doing to the beef industry, so it is not surprising that minimal action was taken to reduce human risk.

The Government's response to the Fifth Report from the House of Commons Agriculture Committee 1989–90 Session, BSE, was simple. It decided to produce an annual report on CJD, to introduce record keeping about calves in Great Britain on a full centralised computer, and to help the rendering industry. But it also decided to continue to permit breeding from cows whether or not they had BSE, to allow feed to contain many things (to be discussed by later committees), to permit current slaughterhouse practices to continue and not to extend the offals ban to animals under six months of age. In the end the results outside the ordinary action of MAFF were minimal.

CHAPTER FIVE

No entry to independent researchers

The names of three important players in the BSE drama have cropped up from time to time in this book in various contexts. I went to talk to them all, knowing that they would have important issues to add to the debate.

Stan Prusiner

I met Stan after hearing him give a talk at the Imperial Cancer Research Institute at Mill Hill in north London. I thanked him for letting me visit his lab in San Francisco the previous year, then asked, 'Do you expect to carry out any research work into BSE?'

'I think my department would like to do that,' he replied, 'but there's the problems of funding, and of getting hold of research time and space. These are big problems at the moment.'

> Ian Pattison, one of the major researchers into scrapie from the 1960s and 1970s, wrote a letter to the *Veterinary Record* complaining about the way in which his work had been portrayed on the media. The problem was that he had found scrapie to be present in the muscles of the goat and this was not to MAFF's liking. In his letter he wanted to make it clear that his findings showed scrapie infectivity to be in the biceps femoris muscle of the goat.

'What's happening later on?' I enquired. Word had been put around that Stan was to be taken off for a steak in town to be asked what he would do about BSE.

'Oh, I'm going to be seeing some people.'

Apparently trying to get information out of Stan is very difficult, whichever side you're on. Some researchers felt that Stan's workers did not quote them in publications (remember: publications are what makes a scientist famous, and fame is an aim). Stan was convinced that the scrapie agent was the prion. Many others were equally convinced, but did not necessarily want Stan to be the one who was proved right. There seem to be a lot of knives out there in the world of scrapie.

It turned out that Stan had been asked by MAFF for information on what research he would do, and what he could do for them, and how much it would cost. He is said to have asked for £3.5 million to sort out many of the problems they were looking at. MAFF had spent a lot of time telling its minister and the House of Commons that there were no problems with BSE, so how could they now turn up and ask for a huge budget to be spent outside the UK? So that one fell flat.

Dave Westaway, an Englishman in San Francisco wrote to *Nature* suggesting that it might be possible to carry out an experiment to see if humans could be infected by BSE. This would involve the human gene for the prion protein being put into a mouse, and then trying to infect the mouse with BSE. Complex. *Nature*, 1990.

Stan Prusiner asked MAFF for the money to carry out the experiment, which was highly important. MAFF turned him down and said he had asked for too much.

Harash Narang

This Indian scientist had been working as a medically qualified microbiologist on the subject of the infectious agent of CJD. He had been concerned with the subject for some time before BSE first hit the headlines, and at the time was probably the only medical microbiologist in the UK who was involved. Harash had been working on potential methods of diagnosis for the disease and had been looking for the infective agent using electron microscope techniques. While working in Newcastle Public Health Laboratory he had established that there were specific particles that were regularly found in the brain of infected animals, and that these could be found using relatively simple techniques. They might even contain DNA.

The data he had gathered was put forward to MAFF, as it was considered that this method could be used to decide which cattle were infected and which were not. He was provided with a group of brain tissues, some of which were known to be from infected cattle and some from cattle considered not to be infected; his results showed some to be infected and some not, and largely agreed with the diagnoses of MAFF. (What was not clear, however, was how MAFF knew that some of the cattle were not infected.) The results were not published, his methods were ignored and he was told indirectly to do no more work on the subject while working for the Public Health Laboratory Service in Newcastle. For a short period he was sent to work at the London Hospital under Professor Almond, a virologist. He could not get into the laboratory unless the scientific technician was there, and information about what he was doing and why was passed to MAFF, who had supplied the technician. By 1993 he had gradually come to realise that the research was not being carried out in a reasonable manner and felt that his work may have been effectively suppressed. Back in Newcastle the laboratory appeared to prevent his research being continued. In the end he was given notice, for obscure reasons. His research went on, however, independently sponsored by a local food manufacturer.

'Do they think I'm just going to give it up because my results don't happen to agree with MAFF?' he demanded. 'Somehow the information must get out that we are eating infected cattle, and yet MAFF seem to be doing their best to prevent this being demonstrated.'

'How do you think I feel about all this?' I said. 'I'm basically being squeezed out of my job, and all I hear from the media is that MAFF officials are telling them I'm producing nonsense. They're even telling them that I'm doing it on behalf of the German Government.' This was something I was particularly fed up with at the time. 'I'm producing good-quality research that isn't open to argument and yet is being denied by MAFF even though it's derived entirely from their results. I can't get it published, I can't even get the major scientists to listen to me. Believe me, if there's anything you think I can do I wish you'd let me know.'

'How about arranging a talk?' said Harash. 'The more people know what's going on, the more they may be on our side.'

'I'll do my best. All I can say is that I have no money and we may have to organise it through local funds.'

He spent four hours one day going through his methods and research with me. Nothing seemed to be incorrectly carried out. Nothing seemed to be strangely interpreted. He may well have been right and had just been trodden on from on high. I came away realising that I had also been misinformed by the MAFF groups who had been telling me that Harash did not know what he was doing. He was actually very good.

We managed to arrange for Harash to give a talk to the British Medical Association in Leeds on 29 March 1995. His problem, like mine, is that although he might be completely right, his work remains unaccepted by the mainline researchers and the journals seem to be fighting shy of anything with a political taint. As a result he has to go around speaking directly to the scientific community, and in this very conservative world anyone who takes that approach is thought of as mildly eccentric.

Helen Grant

The one-time neuropathologist at Charing Cross Hospital in west London had been working on the damage done to the brain by boxing.

As a result she was hounded by the boxing profession and I had some difficulty tracking her down.

£9,114,743 was paid to farmers in compensation for BSE in 1990.

Helen had been following the BSE saga from the start and had examined the actions and speeches of all of the experts and officials involved. 'They knew this was taking place a long time before these apparently "new" cases were reported. The story goes back to 1982 and it's just been a cover-up all along. How can they get away with it?' She was always worried about both myself and Harash Narang. 'It's all right for Lacey to stand up and start throwing mud, but you'll have to keep your head down, Steve. Give your figures to Lacey. Get them published anywhere you can as long as it's a scientific journal. Deal with the media as long as you know they're not just after headlines. This is going to be a long fight and you might be right in the end. But of course the good guy doesn't always end up with the OBE.'

111

CHAPTER SIX

Crystals and flowers: the cause and the answer?

Most schoolchildren today know how to grow crystals from a 'seed' in saturated solutions of salt or copper sulphate. The molecules add themselves at the right places on the growing crystal and make a perfectly shaped, almost diamond-like form that seems to keep the shape of the seed crystal. Now I put over a hypothesis of my own: that the BSE agent was a crystalloid and could therefore have a structure that depended not only on the amino acids that made up the protein (which would be the prion protein) but also on the shape of the crystal. The agent would therefore be able to keep its strain type by keeping its crystal shape, and different strains would have different crystal shapes. This would explain why the agent did not need DNA, and why it was resistant to enzymes and irradiation. It would also explain why the agent could not be destroyed simply by heating but could be removed by microfilters. The simple prion protein on its own would be so small as to pass through filters, whereas the much larger crystalloids would be too large. In Thomas Borage's electron microscopy which I had seen in America there was obviously something that looked like a crystal present in the tissue, attached to the little gold dots that could be seen with the machine. This idea would even explain why the agent grew so slowly in the tissue – it could only grow at the end of the expanding crystal.

I thought no more about it but included it in a résumé of what I had learned on my travels which I sent to those who had talked to me. Later I recalled the idea and decided to offer it to the *Journal of Medical Hypotheses*, which accepted it for publication immediately.

The next year I heard that a French researcher had published the same theory, and Prusiner had mentioned it in his lectures. It was even republished two years later by Joseph Jarrett in the USA, quoting neither my article nor the French one. However, when I looked into the matter further I found that Gajdusek's group had mentioned something similar in a book in 1988, so I had not in any case been the first.

One of the factors that the crystalloid theory depended on was that the chemistry of the prion protein (in the animal that was being infected by the crystalloid prions) should be similar to the chemistry of the prion itself, otherwise the crystal would not grow. For some reason the specific parts of the brain that are affected by scrapie depend on the strain of the disease. Perhaps there was some difference in the prion protein that was produced in different areas of the brain. It then occurred to me that this was of course true; there would be a variation in the chains of sugar molecules that are attached to the prion protein in these different areas.

Dealler and Lacey in Leeds argued that, as TSEs are fatal, not reliably diagnosable, untreatable, and are transmitted from one species to another by the eating of infective tissue, we should not assume the risk from BSE to be 'minimal' as had been stated in a recent *Lancet* article.   *Lancet*, January 1991.

In 1990 I took a walking holiday in the French Alps. Watching scattered cows on the hillsides munching wild flowers, which I suppose would have been a rare sight in Britain, I started to think of the possibility of chemicals in plants being active on the prion. My mind leaped to a *Horizon* programme a year earlier on the subject of glycosidase inhibitors found to be active against HIV. Maybe I'm just not a man with many good ideas so when one hits me it is quite a shock. The chemical group known as alkaloidal glycosidase inhibitors (AGIs) were found in a variety of tropical plants. Swainsonine, found in Australia, was associated with a nervous disease in cattle that ate the plant. Deoxynojirimycin (DNJ), found in the mulberry, was known to be a toxin. DNJ, the classic compound, acted by preventing the break-up of small carbohydrates by enzymes. It also acted on the carbohydrates that were attached to proteins inside cells and effectively prevented the cell from altering these 'glycan chains'. Normally many cells in the body that produce a protein with a glycan chain attached will actually have different chains. The reason for this difference is unknown. The alterations take place on the glycan chain after it is attached to the protein. When DNJ is added, however, all the proteins and their glycan chains are exactly the same. Could the change in the glycosylation of PrP be the reason why sheep catch scrapie? Could it be a potential treatment for any TSE?

Lewin from Toronto has managed to find crystalline bodies inside the mitochondria (power producers inside the cell) of neurones of patients with a disease like CJD. *Lancet*, January 1991.

Paul Brown in Washington had tried to destroy scrapie in many ways. This time he just tried burying it, mixing it with soil in the ground and coming back three years later. It was still there and had lost little infectivity. *Nature*, 1993.

Carp from New York had shown that there really were strains of scrapie. In fact they stayed different from each other after infecting 10 mice, one after another. *Journal of General Virology*, 1991.

No luck at Oxford

When I got back to Leeds I rang up the people at Kew Gardens who had appeared on the programme. The woman who spoke to me invited me to Kew to explain. At the same time I got hold of John Winchester at the Royal Children's Hospital, who had been working on the same compounds, and Professor Y at the Glycobiology Unit at Oxford University. I got the go-ahead from the consultant in my department to visit all these people and set off on a cold autumn evening. In Oxford I also visited Hugh Perry, a neurophysiologist whom I had met at a meeting on TSEs in London. He was one of those who were surprised by just how bad the science had been where BSE was concerned. His lab was involved with the group at the Edinburgh NPU in showing that the prion protein built up in various tissues inside the brain, including some macrophages (such as white blood cells).

Diringer from Berlin managed to demonstrate that dextran sulphate 500 and other similar compounds would prevent a mouse from becoming infected from scrapie. Others had shown that amphoteracin B, a drug used in fungal infections, would do the same if administered at the same time as the infection. *Journal of General Virology*, 1991.

Professor Y had funded the building of the glycobiology unit with a large amount of sponsor capital from Searle-Monsanto Incorporated, the drug company which had made the bovine somatotropin that was used as a milk production booster in cattle. It was a large, bright building, still in the process of being fitted out. I had arrived early and went to talk to some of the researchers to find out what sort of man I was about to meet.

'Don't be too put off,' they said. This was, however, just the thing to put me off. 'He's got enormous amounts of contacts in industry and a lot of access to funding.'

'That's right, but he makes you work spectacularly hard and only picks projects that are going to bring in the money in the end,' added another.

Goldmann from Edinburgh found that the prion protein gene of cattle might vary amongst them. These variations occurred in cattle that did and did not catch BSE. *Journal of General Virology*, January 1991.

Then I went upstairs and sat in the dazzlingly new office with his secretary, thinking over what I would say when I was summoned into his presence. Basically, I was asking for funding and help with research, but I knew it would not be easy: there are all sorts of hurdles in the way. Some researchers hate the idea of someone new working in their subject; they are seen as competition and should be stopped at all costs. But others, the ones whom I in my innocence think of as the real scientists, the ones who actually want to get the answer to the problem and not just the kudos of finding it, are pleased that someone else wants to help.

When I was asked to go in he came straight to the point. 'What can I do for you?'

I explained that I thought the AGIs of plants might be of significance in the pathogenesis or potential treatment of scrapie, BSE or CJD.

'Tell me how.'

'Can I ask you not to release this to anyone else?'

'Well, it depends what it is. It's probable that someone else has thought of it already.' In other words, no, he wasn't automatically going to keep it to himself.

'If anyone has got on to this they haven't published it.' I knew there was no way I was going to get anywhere by not telling him things. 'The chemicals will make the glycosylation of proteins from different strains of cell the same. This will mean two things. The glycosylation will be different from the glycosylation that was previously present on the proteins of any cell, and so may prevent the adding of the protein to the prions inside the cell.'

'Explain that more clearly.'

'The cells that are infected with prions produce a protein, the PrP normally, with normal glycan chains attached to it. This PrP is turned into the prion form by being added to the prions already there in the manner of a growing crystal. The prion is glycosylated in the normal way as well, and so the PrP fits well to it. When the AGIs are added the glycosylation changes and the glycan chains of the PrP will no longer be the same. Therefore the PrP may not fit on to prions that are there already and won't be turned into the prion form. In other words, the AGIs may stop the production of prions.'

'Dealing in death.' In 1990, 255,000 cattle, 528,000 sheep and 590,000 pigs died through accident, disease or old age. Until 1990 knackers would pay farmers £30–£50 for a cow and up to £5 for a calf. Sheep and pigs would be taken away for free. The knackers would then extract tallow, pet food, hides, and meat and bone meal. The competition from other sources of protein has brought down the prices and the renderers, although they used to pay knackers £60 per tonne for bones, now charge £40 a tonne to take them away! And now a knacker charges £40 to take away a cow from a farm. Of 130 knackers in the UK 12 have closed in the past year, and in Scotland both the big companies involved have closed. Some farmers now just dump the animal after removing all its identifying marks. *Economist*, April 1991.

'What was the other thing?'

'Quite simply that if after a while the PrPs that had been modified as a result of the AGI action managed to fit themselves on to the prion, it would be possible to alter them again by stopping the addition of AGI. In other words, the AGI will have an effect both when it is started and when it is stopped, each time by changing the PrP glycan chains. At each turn it may stop the altered glycosylation of the PrP fitting on to the crystalloid form of the prion.'

'So where do I fit in?' he enquired.

'I was hoping that you would be interested and willing to help with research into whether the effect was valid or not. Have you any involvement with infections apart from HIV?'

'Well, some.'

He was certainly playing his cards close to his chest. If I wanted to find out what he was working on, or even if he was interested in my model, it was going to be difficult.

'Have you any connection with CJD or scrapie?'

'Stan Prusiner wrote to me asking if there was a way to make or analyse very small amounts of the glycan chains on the PrP. I told him I didn't think it would be possible to carry it out completely.'

This was obviously only a small part of the story. Everyone was looking for a way by which the prions described by Bolton and Prusiner were able to carry with them some indication of their own factors. There appeared to be strains of scrapie that would produce different incubation periods in mice, and yet there was no DNA in a prion to carry this information. For a long time the California group simply denied that these apparently genetic factors existed. In my article published in 1990 I had suggested that perhaps the glycan chains could act as the apparent genetic factor, and I presume that Stan would have thought of this ahead of me. I later found out that a group in Ontario had carried out an experiment in which they tried to remove the glycan chains from the protein to see if it would still form into prions. They found that it did, and Stan then gave up the hunt for a glycoside-linked factor that would affect the strain of the disease.

That was the end of the conversation. Professor Y basically told me that he was not interested, and I walked away knowing I had been unsuccessful. It is extremely difficult for a person low down on the ladder to walk in and suggest something to the man at the top, especially if it does not agree with his thoughts of the time or does not happen to go in the direction he is wanting. Where do inventors go these days?

Encouragement at Kew

I then tried Kew, where Linda Fellows, the woman I had spoken to on the telephone, fetched Rob Nash, the major AGI man of the time, to make sure that my story got across to him as well. Winchester from the Royal Children's Hospital had not arrived and it appeared that he was going to be late, so they suggested that instead of just drinking tea we could go over everything twice – after all, they were probably going to need to hear it twice just to understand it.

'Scientist ordered to halt "mad cow" study.' Dr Harash Narang had been ordered to stop all work which would verify his claims that he could diagnose cattle with BSE. Such a breakthrough would enable the disease to be detected by perhaps a blood test and permit all infected cattle to be killed. Dr Narang, working at the Public Health Laboratory in Newcastle, said, 'All I want to do is get on with my science but barrier after barrier has been put in my way.' MAFF were accused by David Clark, Labour's food and agriculture spokesman, of attempting to scupper Dr Narang's work by failing to supply promised brain material. In a statement the Public Health Laboratory Service accused Dr Narang of failing to win money from 'the normal scientific grant-giving bodies' and of

---

conducting genetic manipulation without permission. Dr Narang said his experiments would be lost if not completed quickly and he had repeatedly asked the PHLS to register his work with the Health and Safety Executive. The PHLS spokeswoman said the service did not undertake research in this field. *Guardian*, 27 April 1991.

'There appears to be an environmental factor involved in the production of scrapie in sheep,' I explained, expecting to be asked what that was. 'This is the transmissible spongiform encephalopathy of sheep, which scientifically is a very strange condition indeed. We know that it can be transmitted from one sheep to another by inoculating a little bit of infected tissue into another sheep, but we have no idea how it passes from one sheep to another in the real world. A flock may go for 20 years without a case and then there may be three. Another flock may never see a case. We also know that the likelihood of developing scrapie can be increased or decreased by breeding, and so there is a genetic or familial aspect to it. The most extraordinary thing is that there are no cases in Australia or New Zealand, despite their having imported flocks of sheep with the same genes as UK sheep. Some of the imported sheep developed scrapie themselves, but none of their offspring did. It's as if there's something in the environment that either causes it or brings it out in the animal.'

'Has anyone actually brought some of the Australian sheep back to the UK to see if they develop it again? You know, like the restocking of the French vines after phylloxera,' asked Y.

'I've not heard of it, but it would be interesting. Anyway, the disease has appeared elsewhere and has been found to be associated with the land on which the flocks were pastured. In Iceland they had so much scrapie on some parts of the island that they decided to slaughter the flocks and restock from areas that were not affected. A few years later scrapie appeared again in the same places as before.' I

120

was trying my best to get it all over in an interesting and yet scientific way. 'So if we were looking for something in the environment that was causing the disease, and after all it could be anything from a chemical in the rock to a fungus on the trees, it would be reasonable to look for a factor that would cause the production of the infective agent.'

'How do you mean?'

'I mean that the agent produced in the animal kills it by being infective and spreading from cell to cell, eventually damaging such a large part of the brain that the animal dies. That's why, if we take a piece of infected brain and inoculate it into the brain of another sheep it will die too.'

'You've obviously got the idea that AGIs fit in here somewhere,' said Rob. 'Could you give us a clearer idea of where this might be?'

I explained about how the infective agent might be the prion made from the normal PrP protein. 'There are families that have an apparently transmitted form of CJD. I suppose it could be that the mother is infecting the child, or perhaps that the parents are giving a gene to the child, that makes it more open to attack from some external agent. Or – and this is what is felt by a group in California, the gene itself causes the disease. When they looked at the gene for the PrP in families that had the disease, they found they were different from those in 'normal' families. They took the gene from one of the familial human TSEs and inoculated just the gene into a mouse, using transgenic techniques. This meant that every cell in the mouse's body would contain that gene. The mouse developed the disease spontaneously. So, if you can produce the disease in a family merely by altering a few amino acids in a protein, why couldn't you do something similar simply by altering a few glycan chains?'

Health and Safety Executive's directions on the handling of carcasses from cattle with BSE, issued in 1991

'While it is very unlikely that BSE will affect human health, it is important to take reasonable hygiene precautions in handling carcasses of these animals. So when handling BSE carcasses:

- cover cuts and abrasions with waterproof dressing before work starts
- wear protective clothing including gloves
- avoid cuts and puncture wounds during work
- use eye protection if there is any risk of splashing
- wash your hands before eating, drinking and smoking
- wash down contaminated areas with detergent and water
- rinse protective clothing free of debris after use and wash with water and detergent.'

The problem is that the HSE does not seem to realise that many cattle are infected with BSE but show no symptoms, and hence will not be treated as 'BSE cattle'.

They looked at me in a distinctly disbelieving way. 'AGIs don't change genes.'

'No, that's not what I meant. One of the factors associated with the change of normal PrP into the prion form is a dramatic change in its solubility in water and in its ability to be dissolved in oily liquids. What happens when you take off the glycan chains from a protein? It becomes less water-soluble.' When I said it that way it actually seemed fairly unlikely to me, too. 'We're looking for a substance that alters the structure of PrP in such a way that it will tend to change spontaneously into a prion form. This substance must be found in the environment of sheep, particularly on the western edge of Europe, the Danube valley and various other parts of the world. It must be absorbable from the environment and must somehow make its effect inside the body. We are looking, preferably, for a substance that can be eaten, absorbed from the gut, distributed around the body, enter the nervous system and remain in sufficient concentrations to cause an effect on PrP production. Come on! What does this sound like to you?'

'Yes, AGIs would do that, I expect,' replied Rob. In fact he knew that this was not total nonsense because they had already shown that one of the forms of AGI, castanospermine, was absorbed and distributed in this way.

'Have you any specific ideas on which plants to chase up?' asked Helen.

'In all honesty, I don't even know whether any plants in the UK will have any AGIs. What do you think? Is there a chance that we'll find any at all?' My answer wasn't particularly helpful. I was more or less saying that I was going to look for a needle in a haystack.

'Oh yes, I'm sure there will be some. But I can't really say there's going to be one that I would put my finger on as the ultimate evil. The pea family might be a good point to start.'

'Does this sound like a lot of rubbish to you, or does it sound reasonable?' I made it clear that I needed help on this one. 'If I started to look for the AGIs in UK plants, would you help identify any of the chemicals if they turned up?'

It was clear that Rob was interested in this proposal, and I hadn't even explained to them the possibility that the AGIs might not only be a possible cause of scrapie but a treatment for all TSEs as well.

'Well I can't see any problem with that at the moment. It seems worth a look at least.' This, compared to what I had encountered so far, was very encouraging.

When Winchester arrived we went over things again and I travelled back to central London on the Tube with him. He had been examining the activity of some of the AGIs, both synthetic and natural, at the lab at the children's hospital in Great Ormond Street. The big American drug companies had been sending him compounds to try out and he had organised a system by which he could supply them with the results in a reasonably short time. He who has the money will win, and he needed all the money he could muster for his laboratory. So, if the Americans had the cash, and George Fleet, another chemist from Oxford, who was able to construct small amounts of artificial forms of these AGIs, had the push, then Great Ormond St would test compounds in the laboratory for their action in inhibiting enzyme activity. He was interested, too. 'Well, who wouldn't be?' I asked myself, with more confidence than I had felt to date.

Watkins from *Today* Newspaper wrote to the *British Medical Journal*. He had found that people who had received pituitary extracts as hormone replacement were still acting as blood donors and were still carrying donor cards.   *British Medical Journal*, June 1991.

Arya from India wrote to warn that people who had received sheep-brain rabies vaccine might well have been inoculated with scrapie and probably should not give blood. *British Medical Journal*, August 1991.

Research on a shoestring

Soon after that I went to work in Bradford. The doctor in charge of me at St Luke's Hospital there was less often seen as she was attending a management course, and the microbiology consultant at the other hospital in Bradford was overworked. It was clear that, if I was to get this work with the AGIs done, I would have to start quickly and get going with it – but the hospital would probably not actually stop me.

Bovine Spongiform Encephalopathy Order 1991 Statutory Instrument 2246

Further restrictions on the disposal of protein derived from specified bovine offals were introduced. This prevented its use as fertiliser and left incineration and landfill as the only methods of disposal. It did not apply to other tissue, however. The SBOs had suddenly appeared in 1989 in England and Wales and 1990 in Scotland as a cheap, apparently normal food. They could be sold for use in many other things as the law at the time had merely banned their use in human food. Pet food was an obvious use, but the appearance of cats with FSE put paid to that when the government recommended that it was not to be used by manufacturers for that purpose. Exportation to the EC had stopped in March 1990 when the EC realised that the UK was merely exporting the food it would not give its own cattle.

Claims have been made that much of the material had been exported to the third world as fertiliser. This information was given by MAFF to the EC, but the source of information on the subject is very poor and I am told that as much as possible was shipped to European ports to be resold. There is inadequate data on this subject, and as a result the place where BSE will appear next is unknown.

Bradley from CVL admitted a specific case of BSE in a cow that apparently would not have been fed the illness. *European Journal of Epidemiology*, September 1991.

' "Mad calf" death widens BSE fears.' The first case of 'mad calf' disease in a 26-month-old Guernsey heifer born after the feed ban. Kevin Taylor, the Government's assistant chief veterinary officer, said that tests confirmed she had died from BSE. 'We cannot say it was maternal transmission with certainty, but there is a strong possibility.' There had been 23 other previous cases where calves born to BSE mothers also died of BSE. *Guardian*, 1991.

There were a few problems: there was no funding for research work into AGIs, there was no space to carry out the work, and there was nobody locally who could tell me how to do AGI extraction. In the end I decided that I would have to fund the work from my own pocket and ask around for help.

As it happened, St Luke's was only a few hundred yards from Bradford University, which was well known for training pharmacists. I visited the Pharmacognacy Department a number of times and left large packages of data to show that I wasn't going to go away until somebody started to help. A number of the senior lecturers were interested in my project, but they all had far too much work on to actually help. In the end a very helpful Dr Wilson, who could permit the use of part of a laboratory for a short period, decided that it was probably easier to help than suffer the pressure from me. Eileen Lees, a friend who had previously worked at the Leeds Public Health Laboratories, went down to Kew to get directions from Rob Nash on how to extract the AGIs. While there she also fought her way through the massive library, to find out where we should head to look for the plants most likely to have AGIs.

Euan Scrimgeour from the Lanarkshire Health Board and Paul Brown from Washington reported that the actions that took place in an abattoir were potentially risky to the men working there.

'Until recently, part of the slaughtering procedure in cattle entailed opening the cranium with a power saw to remove the brain for processing, with the unavoidable accompaniment of an aerosol. When the policy of discarding the brain was adopted, instead of opening the skull a high-pressure air hose was frequently introduced into the foramen magnum [the large hole in the bottom of the skull through which the spinal cord passes] to force out the intracranial content, and again the production of an aerosol [brain tissue in droplets in the air] was inevitable. More recently, the cranium has been broken open mechanically and the cranial contents aspirated and passed into a closed container.

'Accordingly, until it can be confidently shown that the BSE agent is not pathogenic for man, it would be prudent to recommend that the slaughtermen should wear visors or goggles, masks, gloves and protective clothing when extracting the cranial content from cattle which might have been exposed to BSE.' *Veterinary Record*, October 1991.

MAFF had repeatedly denied that brain contents were ever used in sausages or beefburgers. They had not denied that this material was in meat pies or gravies.

£16,329,348 was paid to farmers in compensation for BSE in 1991.

The lab at the Bradford Pharmacognacy Department was tired, the glassware overused and equipment in short supply. Eileen worked on one of the heavy old mahogany benchtops that must have cost a fortune when first put in, and had a refrigerator and a few cupboards in which to keep things. The plants, initially dried, were weighed and boiled with water. When water had partially boiled off the extract was passed through a column of fine resin beads coated with a substance that would pick up any compounds of the type we were looking for. These compounds were then washed out into a further fluid and concentrated again. The extracts were now tested for their action in inhibiting the ability of specific enzymes (these were the glycosidases).

The enzymes had been extracted from the brain of a sheep's head that I had obtained from one of the halal abattoirs in the area that slaughter meat for the local Muslim population. On a rainy day I had found my way down a muddy track in Leeds – the abattoir could be smelt hundreds of yards away. There were open oil-drums of offal standing at the side, and a portly man who was washing down one of the concrete surfaces just handed me a sheep's head and wished me good luck. The mortuary attendant at Bradford opened the head for me, and the brain was removed and enzymes extracted from its tissues.

Lacey from Leeds reports that the number of cases of BSE in 1991 is already three times that in 1989 and some of the cases were born after the feed ban. He feels that the disease could be becoming endemic.   *Veterinary Record*, February 1992.

Wilesmith from CVL analysed the epidemiological data for BSE. It appeared that a higher percentage of cattle were affected in the south, south-west and east of England than in Wales or the north-west. Scotland was relatively less affected. He showed that cases were much more likely to be in dairy herds than in beef suckler herds (herds where beef cattle suckle their own calves). Purchased cattle in beef herds were much more likely to develop BSE than home-bred cattle. This is probably because the purchased ones were likely to be cross-bred cattle from dairy herds.   *Veterinary Record*, February 1992.

One of the interesting points in this analysis was the apparent peaks of cases in November–March of 1988 and 1989. No reason has been found for this.

These extracts contained adequate amounts of the enzymes to cause a change in colour of a specific compound; the colours produced were fluorescent. Eventually Eileen got so many samples to test at any one time that it was worth taking them all over to the University in Leeds and using their instruments to get an accurate measure of the fluorescence produced. She did everything in triplicate to avoid errors, and included controls in every sample to be sure of her results.

Daisy science

Within a few weeks she had hit gold. I had sorted out some 50 species of wild plant before the weather caught them at the end of autumn. Of all things, Eileen found a strong AGI in the daisy, *Bellis perennis*. I could hardly believe it. Here I was searching all over Yorkshire and beyond for rare species, and what I wanted turned out to be in one of the commonest plants in the UK! We sent the plant extract off to Rob who did a gas chromatography-mass spectroscopy analysis on it. This is a test in which the chemicals are chemically altered to make them evaporate; they are then separated by passing them along a fine column, and as they come out of the tube they are put into a machine that measures the size of the molecule. This equipment is now so good that in the best cases the result appearing on the VDU screen might not only show the quantity of the compound but its exact structure as well.

The following year I collected 250 assorted plant samples from about 230 different species, taking them from permitted places all over Yorkshire. The plants had to be dried before they could be taken over to Bradford for Eileen to carry out the extraction. I remember the children from the neighbouring houses watching me drill holes all over my wooden garage doors to let air flow through to dry bunches of flowers hanging from the ceiling. I also made a large drying box with a strong extractor fan, containing square sheets of supported trays of wire mesh. Soon the room that Eileen was working in was strewn with cardboard boxes full of plant leaves, but she kept on testing and, despite having to move from one lab to another, got everything done in 18 months.

Foster from Edinburgh looked to see if embryos became infected from sheep with scrapie. He infected some ewes with scrapie, artificially inseminated them from uninfected rams, and harvested the embryos five and six days after insemination. The embryos were transferred to uninfected recipient ewes that had been genetically selected for low susceptibility to scrapie. Six of the 26 lambs born to these recipients developed scrapie.   *Veterinary Record*, April 1992.

This was an important report, showing that vertical transmission of scrapie from ewe to lamb took place while in the uterus and during early gestation.

'Friendly fire in medicine: hormones, homografts, and CJD. Paul Brown. *The Lancet*, 4 July 1992.

Humans may have become infected with CJD through work (a neurosurgeon, a neuropathologist, and 2 histopathology technicians), through surgery (12 cases), through neurological tests (2 cases), and through the inoculation of pituitary hormones (>48 cases and rising).

It was found that the purification process for the pituitary hormones did not remove the agent, and even the chromatographic purifications did not either.

Growth hormone from pituitaries was replaced by artificial forms in 1985 but some countries continue to use the dangerous form.

Mayer from Nottingham suggested that the reason why cellular damage took place in prion-infected cells was that the prions were found associated with lysosomes (parts of cells that destroy matter with enzymes). He suggested that this was also true of Alzheimer's disease, and that if there were a way to destroy the action of the lysosomes this might be a potential treatment for both these types of disease.   *Lancet*, July 1992.

Rob worked extremely hard and achieved good extracts from many of the plants that had been successful for Eileen and myself. In the end we found AGIs also in bluebells, and in a number of other plants the AGI effects were so great that the enzymes were completely inhibited.

Jeffrey from Midlothian reported that mice inoculated with the TSE of the nyala, the kudu and the cow developed a TSE the type and distribution of which was the same. This suggested that the kudu and the nyala caught their disease from cattle. *Acta Neuropathologica*, 1992.

Closed doors, closed minds

The next thing was to test the plants on a flock of sheep known to be at risk from scrapie – one in which cases had been known to occur in the past. In order to do this I had to get in touch with the Veterinary Lecturer at Leeds University to see if he would carry out the experiment at the experimental farm near Tadcaster. He was very helpful and said that if the information was available, and if the funding was there, he couldn't see why they wouldn't go ahead. He suggested that I just write down the directives for the experiment and send it to them.

There followed months of writing to various drugs companies asking for funds. All to no avail. BSE was 'not a danger to anyone'. MAFF had told them so, they said, and the independent advisory group headed by Dr Tyrrell had backed them up. It was a very frustrating year. I had to have permission from MAFF in Harrogate to carry out experiments on the sheep. They were automatically obliged to send any applications of this type to the CVL in Weybridge. The result was a bucket of cold water being poured on the idea. They had decided that they knew all about scrapie, and what they knew was that it was caused by an infection.

Eventually the people in Harrogate came back to me saying that if I rewrote the application in a particular way they might consider it; but by that time I was quite simply worn down. The experiments on sheep were never carried out. But we still have the chemicals.

CHAPTER SEVEN

Forceful arguments

Late in 1989 Professor Lacey had been invited to make a speech to butchers, abattoir workers and others in the meat industry at a large hall in Bradford. He asked me if I wanted to go along and listen. It was a very cold night and it was good to get into the brightly lit hall. In fact we got there very early and I found myself wandering round talking to people about what they thought of BSE and the risk to them.

A hostile audience

What came out was that they thought BSE was no risk to them, and that Lacey was the villain of the piece. They were going broke directly as a result, they felt, of what he had said on television. They were going to tear him apart at this meeting.

I sat in one of the front rows and prepared some questions to be on his side, although by that time I thought it was going to be of little use. If there was not a riot after his talk I would be surprised, and there was unlikely to be time for any questions.

Lacey and Colin Maclean, Director General of the Meat and Livestock Commission, sat next to each other in the middle of the stage and had a single microphone between them. Lacey spoke first and told the audience how this was a new disease that was fatal, untreatable and undiagnosable. It could be passed from one species to another, there was no method of immunisation or adequate destruction of the agent, and there was a 70% chance that humans could be infected. He claimed that the numbers given by MAFF for cases of BSE were, of course, the ones you see – what about the ones you don't know about, the asymptomatic ones? They would be infective as well. He told them about the passage of this type of disease to animals just by touching, never mind by eating infected tissue. He told them about the surgeon, the pathologist and the mortuary technicians who had gone down with CJD in this way. Surely there must be a risk to people from the meat trade? Then there was the risk that was being taken by the people eating the food.

By the end things were actually quite quiet. He had put things over in a way that they would be able to understand, and to a degree at least it had got across.

Misinformation?

He was followed by Colin Maclean, whose talk was already prepared and made no reference to Lacey's information. There was no evidence that there was any infectivity in any tissues in cattle outside the central nervous system, he said, and why should we expect there to be? People had been eating scrapie since 1730, and where was the outbreak of CJD as a result of that? BSE was just scrapie in cattle, and as scrapie did not infect humans neither would BSE. The media had merely scared us into worrying. What was all this about meat? None of this group of diseases had been found in any meat, and we certainly should not worry.

I could hardly believe my ears. Had he been misinformed? TSE infectivity had been found in the flesh of mink, goats and hamsters. He also must have been told that, even if BSE was scrapie, it would have changed when it went into the cow and so the range of species it would infect would have changed. Even if scrapie did not infect humans, that was no indication whether or not BSE would.

His was definitely a political speech. He repeated things that he wanted people to remember, and he spoke slowly and forcefully. At the end, however, many of the audience were still worried about what Lacey had said. 'How could Maclean get around it?'

Strong reactions

Various questions, obviously read from scraps of paper prepared beforehand, came through: How could Professor Lacey be warning people about BSE when there was no evidence that BSE infected humans at all? Did he not think he was ruining a good industry for no good reason? Lacey replied that there was plenty of evidence that humans would be infected, but what was missing was proof. The problem was that we would have to wait 20 years for that, and we had to act now or it would be too late. The questioner understood and sat down!

After half a dozen similar cleavers hurled at Lacey, a man at the back stood up and stated that he was obviously taking a reasonable line. We could not prove that BSE was a risk, but there was plenty of evidence that it might well turn out to be one. We certainly could not prove that it was *not* a risk. As such we should assume that it was, and take action now.

After the meeting ended Lacey was surrounded by about 20 people all asking worriedly for advice. I approached McLean, trying to be as calm as possible, and asked if I could speak to him for a minute.

'Certainly. What can I do?'

'I'm working for Professor Lacey and it makes me sad to

hear the argument that is going on. We all know certain data that is true, and I feel that instead of fighting in the media it would be better for us to put our data to you directly.'

'Are there particular things you feel aren't getting through?'

'Well, I'm not sure whether they aren't getting through or are just not felt to be important.'

'Such as?'

'For instance, your statement that infection has never been found in meat. It's been reported from two sources, mink and goats, in the literature. The experiments in sheep were done with very small inoculations into mice – so small that they are very unlikely to show positive results.'

'The result in goats came from a single animal. The mink result has never been repeated. How can we change everything on the basis of two unreliable results?'

'The results may not be excellent, but they were valid. Have you asked the authors of the research whether they felt them to be OK?'

'It's quite clear that there's nothing more we can say to each other.' He was getting hot under the collar.

'Surely some kind of information supply from us must be good?'

'You are the people who are ruining our industry. There's nothing to be worried about with BSE. We're now spending millions to stop misleading information from people like you from damaging farmers. Why should we want to put up with it?'

'Because risk is being taken at the consumers' expense. We feel this risk is morally unacceptable.'

He started to raise his voice.

I can't really remember what happened after that. It seemed to turn into a slanging match, and McLean marched out with his entourage. I was shaken and Lacey invited me back to his house to calm down. He was quite convinced that doing things through the 'proper channels' would be ineffective, as there was simply too much money tied up in the beef industry.

CHAPTER EIGHT

Calculating the human risk

Assessing the risk to people of contracting BSE through their food was going to be difficult. Not only did we not know the amount of the disease in the food that we were eating; we also did not know how much was needed to infect us. MAFF had denied that there was any way to work out the number of infected cattle that we were eating and had stated that all infected animals were either being destroyed when the farmer reported them or, if they were slaughtered before diagnosis, their most infectious parts being thrown away. So was I going to be able to prove any risk anyway?

I had always been aware that if I produced any figures with which the MAFF people could argue, they would simply deny my findings. All my data had to come either from published scientific work or from MAFF's own figures. No assumptions should be made that they had not made themselves, and all data that I used that were estimates would have to be underestimates. If all my findings did not fit within these restrictions, they would be ignored. I could only use their own evidence and fight them on their own ground.

I had heard that MAFF had actually done some of these calculations themselves, but were not telling anyone what their findings were. It seemed that I was going to have to do it all again and publish it myself – it didn't look as if anyone else would.

Caughey in Montana demonstrated that the growth of the scrapie agent in cell culture could be potently inhibited by the addition of congo red. This is a dye used in histology that stains amyloid, the compound found outside cells that contains the prion. *Journal of Neurochemistry*, 1992.

Having now been transferred to York I arrived at a lovely new district general hospital near the city centre. It looked as if my job was to be the signing out of reports from the lab to go to the hospital, telephoning results to people that needed them and walking around the wards looking for clinical infection cases where I could be of value. The only problem was that the standard of practice in York was so high that the number of infections was small, and serious ones were shipped off to Leeds to be intensively treated. The intensive care unit in York was run immaculately, and patients who might have infections were treated well without any need for a junior microbiologist. So where was I going to be?

In 1992 came a directive from the Department of Health that schoolchildren should not dissect cattle's eyes due to the potential risk from BSE.

Bruce of Edinburgh found that BSE could be transmitted to the same mice as could be infected with scrapie, but that the distribution of damage in the brain was different between scrapie and BSE-infected animals. She made it clear that the infection was reliable and regular. *Journal of General Virology*, 1992.

Having made sure that I knew who was boss in the lab, the consultant largely left me to myself. As long as I made sure that my time was not wasted, was aimed at patient welfare and was involved in my training, he was more or less happy. At that time it seemed that more work on BSE was needed as the numbers of cases in the UK was burgeoning, so when I wasn't needed in the immediate work of the hospital I went back to my research.

More research in York

MAFF had refused to carry out a number of specific calculations with its data (or if they had they weren't saying so). They refused to admit that it was possible to work out the number of infected cattle that we would be eating, and stated openly that all infection of significance was being discarded and incinerated. At the time I thought they were probably correct and that the amount of infection we were eating was minimal, but that did not justify the lack of any calculations to show it.

It was decided that enough data would be available to carry out these calculations, and I wrote to John Wilesmith asking him for the latest figures for the number of cases of BSE. This data was in five bands, each band representing the number of cattle diagnosed with BSE reported to MAFF in the separate years 1988, 1989, 1990, 1991 and 1992. The numbers from 1988 and 1992 were not as complete as the others; the law regarding the reporting of cases of possible BSE was only introduced halfway through 1988, and at the time many farmers who saw a case were not at all sure what they were looking for. In 1992 the numbers only went up to November and so missed out not just the last month but also some cattle that had not been fully diagnosed (they had been reported, but their disease had not been confirmed by the histologists). The results were also less than perfect in that many of the ages of the reported cattle were 'unknown'. Sorting them out was not going to be easy.

£29,211,593 was paid to farmers in compensation for BSE in 1992.

I sat and stared at these figures and tried to fathom how I could work out from the number of cases reported the number of cases eaten before symptoms appeared. This was going to be a hard nut to crack for a small brain like mine, and I was going to need a nutcracker.

Getting to grips with the statistics

The University of York was expanded during the 1970s and consists of some glamorous concrete and glass buildings set around a number of artificial lakes on the eastern edge of the city. It was thought of as a place to go if you didn't get into Oxford or Cambridge and was well run with a limited number of specialist staff in specific subjects; one of these was statistics.

I rang the Mathematics department and found that all the people I was looking for were unavailable. Eventually it turned out that Professor Waugh, now retired, retained a small office on the campus and would be willing to talk to me in a few weeks' time. This was not a subject that you could just load into your PC statistics package and press the button in order to get the answer. It would require some brainwork too, and I thought he should find it interesting.

The first essential was to rewrite the results in a way that could be better understood. The year in which the animals were reported did not matter, but it was important to know in which year they were born or infected. There was now good information (as there had been already at the time of the Southwood Report in 1989) that the infection was taking place early in the animal's life, and so the year of birth could be estimated as the year of infection. When

141

these numbers are realigned so that the age of death (due to BSE) is correlated with the year of birth, a more useful pattern can be distinguished. Now it is the same group of cattle being followed (see Table 5). Of those born in 1984–5 some will die at the age of two, some at three, four and so on. The important thing was that you could now see how more and more cattle from the same group would be dying as the cattle became older. Immediately it becomes clear that the most likely age for a cow to die of BSE was five. What actually happens is that every year the number of infected cattle rises dramatically and, for instance, the death rate of four-year-olds in 1991 would have to be compared with that of the five-year-olds of 1992 to get an idea of what was happening overall to the group of cattle born in the same year.

A letter arrived. It was on unheaded paper. The postmark was unreadable.

'Have you looked to see what the USDA feels about BSE? Have you investigated the source of the information that is being sent to the EC? Please destroy this letter.'

Was this a nutcase from the vegetarian lobby or a newspaper trying to create some news? I decided that, since it said nothing new and I knew that the USDA was scared stiff of BSE as it would destroy the meat industry in the USA if it got over there, it was probably not from deep inside MAFF. I tore it up.

Some of the data are inadequate: those from 1988 were not going to be acceptable for statistical purposes. There was no way of knowing what percentage actually got reported to MAFF and in addition, since the way in which the animals were diagnosed changed during this period, a comparison between these numbers and those in the other years was likely to be unsound. The figures in this table for 1992 have been corrected for the estimated number that would be reported in December. The correction assumes that the numbers in December would be at the same rate as in previous months. The numbers have also been adjusted to take account of those cases where the age of the beast was not known by the farmer when it was reported. For this purpose I have assumed that these cattle would take the same age distribution as in those cattle where the age was known. Unfortunately this may be inaccurate, for it is likely to be the older cattle whose ages the farmers did not know. I shall explain later why I have made this assumption.

Now it is clear from the above age distribution that cases of BSE did not suddenly start to appear in 1986. Cattle born in 1983–4 did not just start showing symptoms when aged five; there would clearly have been cases when the group of cattle was younger. In other words there must have been cattle with clinical BSE in 1985 and possibly earlier. It is also clear that BSE is not simply going to stop in 1992 just because that was as far as the available MAFF data went. Cattle born in 1987–8 were still going to develop BSE when aged four, five, six and so on, and so the disease was going to continue in the UK for many years to come. Southwood's prediction of it virtually disappearing by 1996 was optimistic in the extreme; it was just not going to happen.

No professional is impressed by a scientist standing up and making dramatic statements, however true they may be, unless he has the figures to back them up. Just sitting looking at tables of MAFF figures was not going to get me anywhere, no matter how obvious the implications seemed to me. It was important that this data should be published in a major scientific journal as specific figures so that others could see what I had seen.

At least now I could see a way ahead. The next thing was to get a more accurate picture of the total number of cases that would have taken place already; but I just did not have complete data, such as for those that died in 1985. In addition, I needed to work out the number of cases that would take place in later years; again I sat and stared at the data, trying to work out how it could be done.

There were indeed methods for these calculations, but they did not seem to be ideal. One was to assume that the number of cases of affected cattle born in different years had increased in parallel. In other words, if we know the number of cattle that died aged five in four separate years, could we not use those figures to work out the number that would have died aged four? Each year the numbers increased by an identifiable percentage, so it should be possible to work backwards to calculate the numbers in the preceding years (see Table 6).

The more I looked at this, the less happy I was with it. In fact we could work forwards and backwards in the same way, using the data to predict the numbers of cases that would be reported in 1993, for instance. However, the further we got from the figures with which we started, the more imprecise the predictions would be.

Although the numbers of BSE-infected cattle continue to rise, the numbers born in years after the feed ban are dropping. This is claimed as a success by John Wilesmith, the BSE epidemiologist from the CVL, showing that the disease is going away. *Guardian*, 22 March 1993.

Another method would have been to assume that the relationship between the numbers of cases dying at similar ages would be similar in the groups of cattle born in different years. For instance, if it was possible to predict that of the cattle born in 1986–7, twice as many died aged five as aged four, could we not predict that this would be true for those born a year later (see Table 7)? I looked at this and used it to work out both the numbers of cases expected in later years and those which would have taken place before 1987. These figures did not turn out to be the same as those calculated by the previous method. Admittedly they were not far different; none the less, not only could I not state them to be correct, but I would have to admit that their precision would decrease as they got further and further away from the figures from which they were calculated. How much did that actually matter? Wouldn't the figures be getting smaller towards the top left and bottom right of the table? This was indeed going to be heavy stuff, and I decided that a real mathematician was needed.

Anne Begley, an old friend from my days working in Zimbabwe and now based in Newcastle, took me to see Arthur James, one of the world's experts in compounds turned into colours by enzymes.

Bastian from Alabama suggested that the real agent for all the TSEs might be a spiroplasma. Antibodies to the prion protein also stick on to spiroplasmas, they are resistant to many of the things that do not seem to destroy the agent, and they will cause fibrils to form inside infected cells. However, spiroplasmas are destroyed by heat easily and the scrapie agent is not. *American Society of Microbiology News*, May 1993.

'What do I do?' I asked Arthur. 'The data simply won't fit into a statistics range. I can't produce figures to show how exact my data is. All right, I can calculate just how many cases appeared before we knew of the disease, and I can tell you how many are yet to appear, but what I can't do is work out the certainty of the results. You know yourself that unless you can demonstrate precision in your results it will simply be said that the numbers are wildly off target and they have no duty to take any notice.'

'Why don't you just make sure that everything you produce is an underestimate?' suggested Arthur. 'As long as they can't show that any of your figures are anything but an underestimate or are quoted from MAFF or from the published scientific literature, they'll have to listen.' That was exactly what I had been telling myself.

'You'll be lucky to get anywhere, if you ask me,' said Anne. 'They could have produced these figures themselves quite easily and are obviously determined not to allow them to get to the press. In other words they see them as bad for them, and will fight to ignore or discredit them.'

CJD reports in the years have been rising. These figures were from the CJD Unit in Edinburgh.

May 1990–April 1991	1991–1992	1992–1993
32	37	48

The reason for this is given as just an increase in awareness of the disease. They found no convincing evidence that the eating of a range of meat products was associated with the disease. July 1993.

'Look, if I had to assume that the scientists working for MAFF would lie through their teeth in saying that these figures could not be produced or that they were invalid, I would just give up now,' I said. 'The MAFF scientists are understandably proud of their industry. Of course they want to protect it. The ones that I have asked outside the Central Veterinary Laboratory tell me to keep going. They say that if Lacey and I are the only ones making an effective noise about human risk, it's important that we keep going. They are worried themselves.'

'And the harder you try, the more research money they'll get?'

'I suppose that's true, but they're not malicious felons, after all. Lacey doesn't want to destroy the beef industry, either, but he really does feel that that may be the only way to get rid of the disease fast enough to avoid the risk of a long-term human and agricultural disaster. Anyway, however hard I work at this I'm just going to go unfunded, put my job on the line (who wants a boat-rocking senior registrar?), not be able to chase up potential treatments, and the population will continue to risk the lives of their children.' They could see that I was fed up.

'So where do you fit in to this?' asked Arthur.

'God knows. When I look at BSE I see a fatal, inadequately diagnosable, untreatable disease. It's already been passed to 14 species orally, and there's a 70% chance that humans could be susceptible. If a new drug appeared on the market and turned out to have these kinds of features it would be banned instantly. People who had been prescribed it would be tracked down and offered long–term counselling. But with BSE they appear to be determined to hang on. They don't know if there *is* infectivity in much of the food we're eating, so they prefer to assume that there isn't until there is proof that there is. They don't know if the amounts they have found are enough to infect us; they bypass the question by assuming that BSE came from scrapie and as such presents no risk to humans. Assumptions like this are a sort of 'best case scenario'. They are the most optimistic view that you can take. I just feel that as a large proportion of the population in the UK may be at risk, it is my duty as a doctor to do something about it. So few people in the UK know enough about BSE or even CJD to be able to argue with MAFF. It's a horrendous risk they are taking, in my view, but they must have convinced themselves that this is the right direction to take. If I could produce data with which they couldn't argue, then action would have to be taken.'

'You should bring an orange box with you,' said Arthur drily.

'Mind you, I'm not sure you'd find many people prepared to listen,' said Anne. 'They all want their sausages and the kids all want their burgers. You do realise that you won't just be telling MAFF that action must be taken – you'll be saying that they should already have taken that action and that they are responsible for millions of people feeding themselves and their children on potentially fatal foods.'

'Nobody wants to hear bad news,' Arthur commented. 'They'd much rather be told that everything will be OK, and it's often much easier to shoot the messenger than to read the bad news.'

Pressing on with the underestimates

The figures that were reported to MAFF were underestimates in the first place. A farmer had first to recognise that something was wrong with his cow, and that this warranted not being taken to market but being shown to the vet. The farmers were getting better at diagnosis all the time, but the early data would certainly be an underestimate. The vet then had to agree that it was a case of BSE. But vets are not always right, and he could easily have decided that it was something else, something non-notifiable. There are a number of other syndromes that affect cattle with neuro-logical, 'staggers'-type syndromes. The most common ones were magnesium shortage or changes in the amount of glucose in the blood, but there were plenty more from listeria infection to selenium overdose (selenium is found in excess in feed made from rape seed plants). As BSE spread (by 1993 it was the biggest cause of death of cattle in the UK apart from slaughter for human food), vets were becoming more and more likely to accept a case, but early in the epidemic they might often have been wrong.

If BSE was suspected, the farmer would then give up the cow to the veterinary officer from MAFF, who would have it slaughtered and the head removed. A sample of the brain would be extracted through the foramen magnum, the large hole in the bottom of the skull through which the spinal cord passes. If this necropsy sample was taken incorrectly, the resultant tissue would not necessarily show signs of BSE under the microscope. The brain tissue was commonly stained using two stains, haematoxylin and eosin, to make it easier to recognise the brain changes. But such changes were often too slight to be certain. The 'spongiform change', as it is called, does not appear throughout the brain but in specific parts. In BSE the base of the brain is a good place to look for this change, and usually the technique works. One of the problems, however, is that this change is one of the last indications of the disease. If the cow was slaughtered soon after symptoms appeared it might quite simply be too early for positive identification. When a group of mice were inoculated with mouse scrapie and examined after symptoms appeared, only 85% had the classic changes in their brain. So there was bound to be an underestimate of BSE numbers when using simple microscopy to diagnose it. Harash Narang's technique had been left by the wayside for the time being.

So if I were to continue I would make it clear that every estimate used would be conservative. I would assume that all cases showing symptoms were recognised by the farmer, that all cases were agreed by the vet, that all samples taken were perfect, and that the microscopy picked up all cases. When it came to my calculations I would then take the lowest of the results obtained by the different methods suggested above. Things were improving; I would be able to go ahead. But I still needed help.

Mike was a mathematician whom I met occasionally at parties. 'One thing you might try is to see if, during the lifespan of these different groups of cattle, the same *proportion* of them died at different ages. If they did, or if this number changed at a steady rate as the years went by, you could use this to predict what was happening,' he suggested.

'You mean, if 10% of the cattle born in 1985 out of the overall number born in that year that were going to die of BSE did so aged five, and if the same proportion was true for the five-year-olds born in 1984 and 1986, then I could use that to predict the rate for 1982?' I asked.

'Well, it's worth a thought, isn't it?'

'What about producing a distribution of cattle dying at each age for cattle born in each year? Would that be possible?'

'It could be done, but I'm not sure how certain I would be that your underestimate factor could be observed. I don't know that I could be sure that the figures produced for the empty squares could be certain of being under-estimates,' he said. (See Tables 6 and 7.)

'No, of course you can't, but they will be as good as can be produced, won't they?' I asked. 'I mean, this kind of statistical calculation is one of the standard methods used in epidemiology and will produce figures that we ought to presume to be correct until there is evidence that we are wrong, which is exactly what we are aiming for. Won't it be possible to produce some kind of numerical indication to show how certain we are that the figures are as good as we can make them? In other words, these would be the figures that MAFF should have created themselves if they had tried.'

Gajdusek from Washington described the incidence of CJD in Slovakia since the 1970s, with especially high levels in the villages of Orava in the western foothills of the High Tatra mountains near the Polish border. In 1980 a Slovakian doctor called Mitrova also noticed a high incidence of CJD in the Lucenec area near to and across the Hungarian border. Here 30 cases appeared in patients born and brought up in a dozen small villages with a total population of under 1,500. Initially it was thought that scrapie might cause the disease by getting into the food. Then it was found that the affected people had a prion protein gene mutation. This mutation had been around for quite a long time, however, and many people with the mutation were not showing signs of disease. Indeed, quite old people with it were not unwell.

So now the question was to find what other factor apart from the genetic change was needed to produce the outbreak, and why this factor had appeared now. *Spongiform Encephalopathies,* Churchill Livingstone, 1993.

The fact that not all the members of a family that carry the gene for CJD develop the disease is interesting, and has been noticed also in London.

'You know, Steve, I can't believe they haven't done this themselves.'

'To tell the truth, I've been speaking to one of their people and it seems that they have. Perhaps they just don't want either the Tyrrell Committee or the media to know it – it just doesn't make sense. I actually wonder if MAFF's internal committees on the subject have been filled in properly either. It seems that CVL have produced predictive figures for BSE for the next few years and given them to MAFF. These can easily be used to calculate the number of infected animals that are being eaten.'

'Wouldn't this guy be shot at dawn if it was found out that he'd been handing out information like that?'

'Somehow I doubt it. Quite frankly MAFF and ADAS have been run on an open basis for a long time. Although you have to sign a 'keep it shut' form when you join as a civil servant, much of what they know is simply interesting science and only matters in that some people will make more money than others if information gets out.'

'Yes, but this is one where millions may actually die.'

'We still don't know that, Mike, and if I was to go around saying it before a properly scientific, peer-reviewed paper had gone to press, I should be shot myself. Remember, I don't have Lacey's position to fall back on. No, the fact is they simply aren't used to their data being national secrets, I think, and anyway this bloke only told me he thought they'd worked the data out – he wasn't sure of it.

He certainly agreed it could be done adequately using the sort of method you suggested.'

'So they couldn't argue?' he asked in a cynical tone.

'I'm sure they'll argue anyway, but they can't win, can they?

'You're a hopeful man.'

'Maybe I am, but I've met the researchers in the subject and they should back me up.'

ADAS, the Agriculture Development and Advisory Service, is a national service and part of MAFF. It has local offices all over the country and its aim is to improve the output of UK agriculture. It was originally either free to the farmer or very cheap. Over the past few years attempts have been made to make it self-financing, and so increased charges have had to be made. But, understandably, farmers don't like to pay for advice.

'A very hopeful man. By rights this sort of data should topple governments, you know. So they'll fight it every inch of the way and will have convinced themselves that it's rubbish. Anyone who backs you up will be putting his job on the line.'

'Will you produce the statistics?'

'Yes, I'll do it. But don't tell anyone it was me.'

Weissmann from Zurich and his group tried to take out a gene from a mouse so that it could no longer produce the prion protein. When they did this they found that the mouse could no longer be infected with scrapie. They also found that not only were no symptoms produced but no prions were made either. When they then put a prion protein gene back into the mouse they found it was very easy to infect the mouse with hamster scrapie if the new gene was the same as found in the hamster. Another interesting thing was that the mice without the prion protein gene developed normally and behaved normally. This makes the normal function of the protein even more difficult to guess. *Spongiform Encephalopathies*, Churchill Livingstone, 1993.

This was very important in that it showed that the prion protein was central to the infective agent.

Two weeks later Mike had produced enough data for us to look at and invited me over to discuss the figures with him. I brought my original figures, calculated number by number, and compared them. It looked as if the number of cases for cattle aged two was getting to be too low for calculation before 1988, and that his method would not extend that far. However, the rest of the table came out with perfectly good data which on the whole agreed with my earlier findings.

'So, using three methods of calculation, some of which overlap mathematically, in certain ways we have produced fairly steady figures,' I pointed out.

'Hard work. My PC was getting slow with all the maths that was needed on the spreadsheet. Anyway, I'm happy that the data is valid, which is what's needed.'

'So what does it show you?'

'It shows that the disease had been going on for a lot longer than they have admitted and that it will still be here in 1999. That, by the way, uses one of your underestimation assumptions – that no cattle born after the feed ban will ever develop BSE.'

'Yes, that's right. I want whatever appears in this paper to agree with MAFF's stance on the subject. In reality we're quite aware that there will be plenty of cases born after the feed ban, and Lacey is starting to say that he thinks the disease is passed from cow to calf.'

'Is it?'

'I doubt it. At the moment there doesn't seem to be adequate evidence that it is, and anyway I can think of other reasons why BSE could be passed to the cattle born after the ban.'

'So you're arguing over this with Lacey, I take it.'

'No, I'm not. At the moment we just don't have enough data to say who's right. If you aren't going to win, don't fight.'

'You're just a creep, then,' he said. That made me laugh, if a little ruefully.

'Lacey's been right all the way through so far, so I'm not going to fight him now. If I was in Government I wouldn't fight Lacey. He usually wins in the end.'

Statistics and spreadsheets

Mike's data made me feel much better. This was the first round. What was needed now was to find out how many cattle incubating BSE we had eaten and were going to eat in the future. Yet another brain-crushing problem. Before I could even start, I needed information on the total number of cattle in the UK and their age distribution. These seemed to me in my innocence the sort of facts that could be looked up in an encyclopaedia or searched out in a textbook or manual, but despite a lot of library work I could not find adequate figures. There was no demand by government bodies for cattle numbers to be reported or for animals sold at market to be recorded in a central register. A number of central agencies were eventually going to prove helpful in my search.

The first was the Milk Marketing Board (now Milk Marque). I rang them up and spoke to one of their information officers, who came back to me within 24 hours with the number of cattle producing milk in the UK and their age distribution. I checked this against the amounts of milk produced in the UK and the output per cow of different ages. For instance, if one cow produced 35 pints a day and the UK production was 35 million pints, then 1 million cattle would have produced this quantity. These figures broadly correlated, taking into account the different levels of production throughout the milking year and the lower productivity of young and older cattle.

Of course the calves that we export in such large numbers (about 400,000 per year) to Europe are principally a by-product of the milk industry. In order to get a milk cow to lactate she must first have a calf. After this the milk production is very high but it wanes towards the birth of the next calf, without which she would generally stop lactating altogether. The human population now expects its milk, cheese and yoghurt to be ready and available throughout the year and to order. As a result, cattle are giving birth in all months of the year, and although there is a peak in the spring and autumn this is nowhere near as prominent as it used to be.

Cattle in the UK are generally inseminated artificially these days, with a choice of semen from top-quality bulls. Of course you don't know whether the offspring will be male or female (AI technology has yet to stretch that far), but you will have a good idea of the aspects of the animal. The average milking cow lives about six years, which implies that one-sixth of the herd will be slaughtered every year. As only four of the six years will produce a calf, one out of four inseminations is required to produce a replacement milking cow. That means that two of the four inseminations need to be with milking cow-type semen, as statistically one of the two will produce a male calf. Holstein-Friesian cattle are the breed of the day for milking, but the other two calves will be bred from a mixture of genes from the milker dam and a beef breed bull. An annual bit of maths for every farmer.

Also in the UK there are a lot of herds that are only kept for producing beef cattle; these make up 30–40% of the total UK herd. To get the data on the age and number distribution of the beef calves and beef cattle was more difficult. The Meat and Livestock Commission at Milton Keynes kept large amounts of data but seemed to be developing into less a helpful office of central government and more a privatised body whose job was simply to sell British beef. They have no responsibility to MAFF any more. Despite this a number of MLC people proved helpful and produced data for the last 10 years on the number of cattle in beef production in the UK.

ADAS was also becoming semi-privatised. Instead of their providing a free advice service to farmers, a fee was being introduced, and this was cutting their work dramatically. It was sad, considering just how effective they had been in the past. It was through ADAS that I had got hold of MAFF's data on the age distribution of cattle. Their data was obtained by taking a sample of cattle from known farms and multiplying it by the number of farms in the UK. I checked it against the number of cattle slaughtered in the UK annually. I knew that, as the bovine population was relatively steady, the number slaughtered would be the same as or at least similar to the number born, after taking into account live exports and imports.

The result was a number of sources for the age distribution data for cattle in the UK, and is shown in Table 8. Further information seemed to indicate that the number of cattle in the UK had dropped only marginally since the start of the BSE epidemic, so the figures would be adequate for my purposes.

Now for the *coup de grâce*. It would now, I hoped, be possible to calculate the number of cattle that would have died of BSE had they not been slaughtered for food. This was a standard epidemiological technique which I hoped would take only a few days. It all hinges on the fact that you simply cannot know which cattle are *infected* with BSE when they are slaughtered, and so there is no way of deciding to slaughter the ones that are or are not incubating the disease. In other words it is a random choice. (The exception is that some cattle are selectively slaughtered when young and some when older, specifically male calves.) From looking at MAFF data it was clear that the male offspring from dairy herds were just as likely to develop BSE as female ones, but many of them would be exported as calves to be reared in crates for veal in the Netherlands, Belgium and France. In beef herds the cattle were less likely to develop BSE in specific age groups and so my calculations should take this into account. Any specific effects of this must be taken into account in the calculations, as must any variant that could allow MAFF to see a way of discounting the results.

In the end it took me over a fortnight rather than a couple of days, because I was not familiar with using the spreadsheets on the computer and had to have the numbers checked by people who knew how the system worked. What on earth it would have been like in the pre-computer age I hardly dared to contemplate. I began to envisage the fifties as an era of worn-down pencils and endless sheets of paper.

Mathematically the export of many male calves did not seem to be particularly significant, as they were picked randomly from all those sent to market. The effect of the different ages of cattle in beef herds was not great either, partly because the ages were not in fact all that different, and partly because the numbers of infected cattle in such herds were not large.

I tried to keep the consultant in the microbiology department in York up to date on the calculations that I was carrying out.

'It looks like the number of cattle that we're eating which would have gone on to develop clinical symptoms of BSE had we not slaughtered them is about six times the number that we knew to have the disease,' I told him.

'Is that a lot?'

'Not really. We're talking about humans eating about 500,000 infected cattle. That probably sounds a lot but it's actually not that much, because, if you take the UK population as being 56,000,000 it would mean that we'd only have eaten about one hundredth of an infected cow each.' I showed him the graph of the numbers of cases of each different age group that were slaughtered for food.

'But will all of those actually be a risk to humans anyway?' Dr Anderson was a very clever man and I intended to take notice of what he said. 'The meat producers are already throwing away most of the most infective tissues from the carcass. Where does that leave us?'

'That's a calculation which I still have to do. We may well find that the amount likely to be in the tissues we're eating is minuscule anyway.'

'Interesting stuff.' He hesitated. 'But I must say I'd be unhappy if anything was published that we couldn't back up with sound data. This may be a political problem in the newspapers, but as far as this department is concerned it must remain scientific from beginning to end. And bear in mind that it's all right for Lacey to be on the TV but you need a consultant job some time and that's not the way to get one.'

Never a truer word . . .

Abattoir practices

In producing figures of the numbers of cattle that would have died of BSE had they not been slaughtered first I had to take into account that some of those would actually have been slaughtered because of other diseases, and would not have reached the human diet at all. This was thought by the Meat and Livestock Commission to be between 2% and 3%. The next thing was to work out at what percentage of their natural life expectancy the cattle that would have developed BSE would have been slaughtered, whether they had symptoms or not. This was in fact remarkably easy and came through after a few attempts with the spreadsheet. Of course each of these calculations had to be carried out separately for each year of birth of the cattle, from 1980 to 1988; the computer churned out more and more statistics.

It quickly emerged that one of the most important factors was whether or not we should assume that various tissues were in the human diet. We would obviously still be eating every part of the cow except those parts that were actually banned: everything from the eyeballs, which might be found in sausages (and contain good protein), to the long bones, which contained gelatine for sweets and factory-made foods. The lungs, the nerves and the lymph nodes would all be there, even though what we generally think of as beef would be the muscle, the liver and the kidney.

It is difficult to describe just how effective the abattoirs really are at using as many of the parts of an animal as possible for food. Before the Specified Offal Ban (SOB) in 1989 we would probably also have been eating gut, spleen, thymus, tonsils, brain and spinal cord. Much of this was in fact denied by the MAFF representatives, who said that cattle brain was never used apart from young animals'. Part of the reason was the difficulty in removing the brain from the older cattle, which had stronger skulls, but it was also partly because there was a market for calf brains as a delicacy. What MAFF perhaps did not realise was that machines exist to remove brain from older skulls to be turned into commercial gravy and incorporated into other foods. I had visited an abattoir where such a machine was still present and had been used specifically for this purpose both before and after the SOB.

One of the most worrying factors of the abattoir processing of beef was the mechanical removal of meat from bones. This method was used to extract the last possible fragments from them for use in foods where the precise shape of the tissue was not obvious: meat pies, sausages and beefburgers, for instance. This mechanically recovered meat (MRM) contained extra calcium from the bones it was scratched from, and also quite a lot of protein. In other words it was quite nutritious and worth the abattoir's time and money to remove it. A number of groups were worried that this might actually be where the greatest risk to humans lay. In 1989 for instance, Richard Kimberlin, a member of the Tyrrell Committee, had expressed his unhappiness that this was continuing.

I decided to try to get as much information as I could on how each of these tissues was removed and how large a part they played in the UK diet. This proved much harder than I had expected. Information on the standard weights of various tissues per cow was almost unavailable for anything that did not have a specific price. The weights of nerve tissue were not in any textbook, and the thought that I might find the amount of lymphoid tissue was no more than a joke (see Table 11). I tried getting hold of the organisation in charge of buying and selling offals at Smithfield. They were unhelpful. Offals were largely just 'offals' and were not weighed individually. I went to a good science library and tried to work my way through the veterinary textbooks of offal usage. Despite the fact that many of the offals were used for specific purposes in human food, weights were not all available. It looked as though I was going to have to assess human risk assuming that we ate nothing but liver, kidney, muscle and nerve. Certainly in other animals muscle and kidney carried some of the lowest infectivity levels; as these results would therefore be dramatic underestimates of the true amounts of infection we were eating, MAFF would, I hoped, not be able to argue. All the other tissues were missing from my calculations and some of those – bone marrow and eye, for instance – would certainly be ex-pected to be infective.

The abattoir workers had said that they used all the

nerves that they found. Some would stay inside the meat and some would be chucked into an offals bin for use in animal food or 'something else' (they did not know what the offals-man did with it). It is one matter getting workers to say things but quite another finding them in textbooks. For the sake of my underestimation defence, I decided that my calculations would be based on only 10% of nerve being used in human food.

We simply did not know how much infectivity was likely to be in the tissues of the cow that were turned into meat products. The experiments needed to test this had not even been started, never mind concluded. These techniques depend on a small amount of the tissue to be tested being inoculated into the brain of an animal of the same species known to be uninfected at the time. It has to be the same species because of the species barrier. As explained in Chapter 1, when a TSE is inoculated into a different species it requires a markedly higher amount of disease to effect its transmission. In addition, the incubation period is longer, and, after symptoms have appeared, the appearance of the brain under the microscope is often unlike that of other TSEs. This is why we are expecting to find that mice inoculated with BSE may need a remarkably large amount of the tissue to contract the disease, an effect which may give the impression that some tissues do not contain any infectivity at all. The true reason would be that, in order to become infected, the mouse needed more agent than was inoculated. Unfortunately, because of the time and cost involved, the true experiment for the infectivity of bovine tissue would be to inoculate it into cattle.

'Can you imagine trying to inject a cow brain with diluted liver, Prof?' I said to Lacey. 'It would cost a fortune if nothing else. Each tissue would have to be diluted by 10, 100 and probably 1000, and each dilution inoculated into five cattle. To find the infectivity of brain tissue they would probably have to dilute it one part in one thousand million before the inoculation.'

'That's a lot of cattle, I suppose, but we are talking about a risk being taken with the lives of millions of people? It's easily worth it. If the MAFF junior staff keep up the pretence that there can be no risk to humans, how are they supposed to sell the idea of good scientific practice to the people with the money?'

A letter arrived. It was on unheaded paper. The postmark was London. 'Have you thought what must be wrong with the cattle that are diagnosed as not having BSE by the histology of necropsy samples? Has there been an epidemic of listeriosis? I doubt it. Please destroy this letter.'

This was quite a shock. The person who wrote it must have been involved in the subject. Lacey and I had discussed the problem of the cattle that were diagnosed as BSE clinically but a sample of their brain, when inspected under the microscope, disagreed. They must have had something wrong with them, surely. As the epidemic of BSE had progressed the percentage of histological negatives stayed roughly the same at about 85%, but the number of cases reported rocketed. In other words there had been an epidemic in whatever was wrong with the 15% of negatives as well, and this was unacceptable. The most obvious reason is that much closer to 100% were in fact suffering from BSE, but the histology technique was not good (and this is just what would have been expected from experiments with scrapie and mice). Whoever sent the letter knew that the MAFF reports would be unacceptable.

Professor Lacey was perfectly right, of course. All the way through the episode farmers had been told not to worry, the supermarket customers had been told that all they saw on the television and in the papers was to be ignored, and the politicians had been told what they wanted to hear. How could a scientist demand that at least 500 cattle be destroyed in an experiment which might end up showing that we should not be eating any beef at all? We were both sure that MAFF would not inoculate any beef tissue into a cow early just in case it did show signs of infectivity. They had been furious enough when the group at Northwick Park Hospital had inoculated two marmoset monkeys with bovine brain and found that both of them had developed a TSE.

At this point all I could do was base my calculations of the amount of infectivity in the bovine tissues on the amount found in the tissues of other species on which the experiments had been carried out. By rights this data only existed for mice, mink and hamsters. There were data for goats and sheep that would be underestimates (because they were tested in mice). Some points now came up that I could not simply ignore. One was that nobody had actually defined the amount of infectivity in the tissue of sheep with scrapie. What they had done was to inoculate small amounts into mice in order to find the number of IU in the tissue. As they knew themselves, this simply does not work and you have to know how many IU are needed for a sheep to infect a mouse. This may well be anywhere between 10 and 10,000 IU; no reliable data is available to say. So all could do was assume that the answer was 1 IU and that mice were perfectly sensitive to scrapie, even though this is extremely dubious and the results would be expected to be very low – in other words, not many mice would become infected. All the figures for the various tissues of the body were brought together in a single table (see Table 9).

One thing which could be seen quite clearly was that when infected tissue was tested on an animal of the same species the amount of infectivity was relatively high, and when it was tested on another species it was low. It was also clear that levels of infectivity could be hundreds of times higher in one species than in another. For instance the amount in the brain of the hamster (tested in hamsters) was millions of times as much as in sheep (tested in mice).

Another problem with the available data was that in some species the experiment had simply consisted of inoculating an animal with a known amount of tissue and then observing the animal to see if it developed a TSE. If it did, the only conclusion that could be drawn was that there was enough agent to infect the animal in that one amount. In fact there might have been quite enough in one thousandth as much, but the experiment had not been taken that far.

As a result of such inadequacies, the results were all likely to be underestimates or simply poor calculations. So there was going to be no clear way to pick from the results in these animals a level that I could reliably expect to find in cattle. The only thing I could think of that might be valuable was to take the highest and lowest of the levels from these results and use both to indicate a range between which we should expect to find the infectivity of the cow. Tough stuff, and not particularly satisfactory. I only hoped that I could find enough data from the scientific literature to support my conclusions and keep everyone happy.

A meeting on transmissible spongiform encephalopathy was held at the Royal Society in London in September 1993. I had offered to put up a large poster to encourage people to come up and ask questions about the science. The information on my poster concerned the true number of infected cattle that we were eating, and showed, by gross underestimation that this would be about 500,000 up to the end of the year 1999.

I stood around and waited for my first client to move in. Gradually all sorts of well-known scientists came past before and after the major speeches. Some, like Mark Purdey from the West Country, were friendly and interested, asking me to explain the mathematics behind it all. The MAFF brigade were not so joyful. Chris Bostock, an associated scientist, looked grimly at the figures and wanted to argue them away. The problem was that the numbers were so hopeful that I couldn't rationally argue them any lower. The true figures would have been much bigger.

I gave out some of the ties that I had left behind when I went to America, and this deed was reported in the *Guardian* the next day: 'Stephen Dealler . . . set up a little stall in the lobby, and presented rather fetching ties to any scientist who would accept one. Very striking, blood red, design of a very parrotose cow, lying on her back with her legs in the air, and the motto: *hodie mihi cras tibi* – me today you tomorrow.' This was unlike the information on my boards, which didn't get into the news at all.

Further empty assurances

Meanwhile, MAFF had stated categorically in the literature, the press and the television that there was no sign of infectivity in any tissues that we were eating. This in my view was grossly incompetent. I could not understand whether it was just aimed at calming down the consumer, as they had tried to do over the listeria affair, or whether they actually believed what they were saying. In the case of listeria, as soon as the data was produced that showed the cook-chill food to contain the bacterium the Central Public Health Laboratory had been asked by the media whether this was of any significance. The CPHL, being a perfectly honest bunch of people, told them what was in the scientific literature: yes, it was a pathogen but the number of major outbreaks associated with fatalities in various parts of the world was low. At that point MAFF immediately demanded that the CPHL should not answer any further questions on food microbiology and listeria. They denied that listeria was a bacterium that produces disease, they denied that it was in the food, they denied that it was significant anyway and certainly that it had been involved in a food-poisoning outbreak in the UK.

All these answers were incorrect, and over the following month, as the press got bored with the subject, they admitted the truth. In the current situation they were, of course, telling the truth by saying that there was no evidence of infectivity in bovine tissues. There was no proof because the experiments had not been done; there were no results to give weight to either side of the argument. All that anyone could do was look at the infectivity in the tissue of other species with similar diseases.

When you do this a different picture is immediately seen. Infectivity has been reported at some time or another in virtually every tissue that has been tested. Infectivity had been found in the meat of goats and mink. The meat of hamsters had also shown signs of infectivity, but the data had never been published. The US researcher who had found it in the hamsters had not thought his findings newsworthy enough to submit to a journal.

These levels of infectivity were obviously the ones that had been found at the time when the animal showed clinical symptoms. Mice often just died overnight. With the goats and sheep there tended to be increased difficulty in walking, a change in the way they associated with the rest of the flock, shivering of the skin and an increased tendency for the animal to scrape itself against posts or other animals. What actually mattered to the human population of the UK (assuming optimistically that all cattle with BSE symptoms are reported) was how much infectivity was present in the early stages of the disease, before the cow appeared in any way abnormal. These were the cattle that we would be eating, and if it could be shown that there was likely to be little infectivity in them anyway we need not even start worrying.

Testing brains and spleens

This was a question which had been asked from the early days of major research into scrapie and the diseases that it produced in various rodents. Eventually, despite the daunting amount of work involved, the experiments were carried out. A group of animals was inoculated with the corresponding TSE; members of the group were then taken away at fixed intervals, up to the time that symptoms appeared, for their tissues to be tested for the infection. The cost of carrying out this sort of test is so high that in the main they were limited to the brain and spleen, both of which were known to become highly infective by the time symptoms appeared (see Tables 12 and 13). You can see clearly from these that the levels rise rapidly in the spleen from the early stages of the disease but the brain appears to be relatively unaffected until later – probably 40% into the incubation period.

So we know how the infectivity levels rise in the spleen and brain during the disease, and we can have a good guess at the levels to be found in liver, kidney, muscle and nerve by the time the BSE infection becomes apparent to the farmer. Can we assume that the levels in these tissues rise in a similar way to the spleen and brain during the incubation period? At the moment there is no counter-information and we must assume this to be true. We do know that liver and kidney are infective fairly early on, and it is likely that it is the immunity tissue in these organs that holds the infective agent. It seems reasonable, therefore, to suppose that they follow the path of the similar tissue in the spleen. Similarly the peripheral nerves are directly connected to the brain and spinal cord. There is a continuous flow of fluid around nerves, and experiments show that fine particles inside the nerve could travel from one end to the other in a few days. On this evidence I chose to assume that in nerves and muscles – which would, of course, contain nervous tissue – infectivity would start to rise at the same time as in the brain, relatively late in the incubation period, and to rise parallel to the brain tissue infectivity to reach the highest or lowest level found in the nerves of other species.

I discussed my methods with a number of other scientists. Some told me that my results would be such under-estimates of infectivity that they were not certain they would be useful. Others said that MAFF would deny the results anyway, no matter how conservative they were, and despite the fact that MAFF should have carried out the same calculations themselves. It was all very discouraging.

Kirkwood from London Zoo announced that five out of the eight kudu had developed a TSE. *Veterinary Record*, October 1993.

What have we all been eating?

The next stage was to work out just what proportion of the beef being consumed would be from infected animals. Extraordinary studies had been carried out in the USA to assess what quantities of sausages and beef people ate, smaller experiments had been done in the south of England looking into the amount of specific foods in the human diet, but the best material was the work done by the University of Dundee. It seems that Scotland is now the place to go if you want a heart attack – medical researchers there decided that if this was due to diet they had better find out just what people were eating.

A similar study had been done in Finland, looking into the fat content of meals. The researchers there had concluded that milk and beef fat were the sources of the fat that was clogging up the arteries of those who had had a high proportion of it in their diet for many years. Finnish government action has caused the country's coronary artery disease rate to fall dramatically, leaving Scotland at the top of the pile.

From the Meat and Livestock Commission I knew just how many sausages, meat pies and so on were being consumed, together with their meat content. From the same source I knew just how much liver and meat were eaten, and from Dundee I knew just how much different groups of the population actually ate. The results were shocking (see Table 14). Some people ate beef products in three meals a day, every day! A few people ate almost none. The majority ate one meal a day which included beef or a beef product. There was unfortunately inadequate data on the part that beef played in the diet of children. I tried to get full data about school meals, but this was just too difficult and the results were not at all easy to interpret. In the end I only had enough data to extend to the 37 million adults in the UK between the ages of 16 and 57. The amazing thing was that the assessment from Dundee of the amounts of beef that this group would be expected to eat actually turned out to be very similar to the information from the MLC for the total diet of adults in the UK! To find that the data would cross-correlate was a good sign and encouraged me to push on.

I now had figures for the percentage of bovine tissue consumed which came from infected animals, and for the percentage which came from animals slaughtered at specific percentages of the incubation period, and I had a good idea what level of infectivity we should assume to be in that tissue. I had to put all this together for the groups of consumers according to the different amounts they ate, and work out how much infection each of these would have eaten in total. This was hard work, and if it wasn't for the spreadsheet I would have run out of paper.

The results

As I started adding up the numbers it became clear that various groups would have eaten in total quite enormous amounts of infectivity. By July 1993 the results were ready and the paper largely written. One of the problems with the results was that they did not say whether or not we were going to get an outbreak of CJD in humans. All they did was illustrate the level of risk of this taking place. We have no way of knowing whether humans are easy to infect. If we only need to eat 10^4 IU to become infected, there will be a lot of people affected whether cattle tissues are highly infective or not very infective. However, if we need to eat 10^8 IU, then only if cattle tissues are relatively highly infective would anyone run a risk at all. At that time there was simply no way of knowing (and there still isn't) which of the results in Table 15 is the one we should be expecting to take place. Here we have 21 different possible figures, and only eight of them are zero; the rest are in thousands or higher. The fact was that these were the lowest results that could have been produced, taking all modifying factors into account. We still do not know which of the results should be taken as the most likely. Maybe we should be presuming that cattle are carrying little infectivity in their tissues, and maybe we will need a large dose to infect ourselves; in which case everything is probably all right. However maybe the reverse is true, that cattle with BSE are highly infective and that we need relatively small amounts to become infective. In this case there would, if humans could be infected with BSE at all, be a massive epidemic of CJD either later in the century or more likely early in the next. Since we did not know which of the possibilities was the right one, to presume the more favourable of the two was ethically unacceptable.

This was fairly damning stuff for MAFF. They had stated that we could not know how many infected cattle we were eating. In fact that was quite simple to calculate with a desktop computer. They had said that we could not even guess the risks to humans but that their advisers thought these were very low. In fact the data in the literature plus MAFF's own statistics on BSE showed the risk to be frighteningly high. Somehow I had to get this published.

'You won't get it into any of the major medical journals,' warned Lacey. 'They'll just turn it down after sending it to a reviewer who will tell them that he didn't understand the statistics but it was "inflammatory" and "politically aimed".'

'But it's neither. It's the best that can be done with the figures that we have, and MAFF surely must have already done it themselves.'

'Believe me, you'll be lucky.'

'I've shown the article to about 20 people now, including two mathematicians, and they can find nothing desperately wrong with it,' I said. 'All I've had back is advice on the way it should be written.'

I sent a copy of the article to a member of the Tyrrell Committee, who returned it with some useful comments in June. It was suggested that I put it over in a way that was easier to understand, and that the figures should be set out more clearly because at the time they were almost incomprehensible. A justification was required for the way in which various risks were added up. Otherwise much of the advice was minor, and I tried to use it to put the article in a more acceptable form. Then I sent it off to the *Lancet* . . . and waited . . . waited.

A question of theft?

I spent a lot of time after that doing research and writing letters to people. The technical staff at the Children's Hospital laboratory were helpful, and would have been even more effective if just given the chance. While I was there the reply from the *Lancet* arrived at last: it merely said that my article had not been accepted. If I send an article to a major British journal with as good results as are available at the time, showing that there was a major risk to virtually the entire population of the country, I would normally expect to get it accepted for publication. I

171

decided to talk to them. However, the editor's answers to my questions about what was wrong with the article threw no light: 'Well, it was a tough publication to take on and we decided that it wasn't really for us.' Furious, I decided to try elsewhere. And since the *Lancet* never returns manuscripts to the author I was going to have to rewrite it from my computer files in a format that would be acceptable to another journal.

Back in my office I sat down at the computer terminal and looked through the set of discs sitting in their small white plastic box. None looked to be the right one, which was labelled 'BSE 1'. I tried a few discs in case it had somehow got mislabelled data file – nothing. I just had to admit that it was not in the box or hiding behind an assumed name. Maybe I had left it on the desk. Maybe it was in the car. Maybe I just hadn't brought it with me.

I searched anxiously for about half an hour before giving up and accepting that the disc just wasn't there. Either it had disappeared or I had left it at home. I resigned myself to the fact that if I was going to send off the article I would have to rewrite it manually into a new computer file, so I started to look out the printed copy. It was not there either. In the end I spent about three hours searching the room for these two articles; yet I knew in reality that I had seen them in the room earlier in the week. Certainly they were no longer there now. Nothing else seemed to be missing. Various pieces of quite expensive equipment were untouched, and there was no sign of anyone having broken into the office or laboratory.

My imagination went into overdrive. I rang Professor Lacey in Leeds. 'What do you think I should do? The stuff must have disappeared from my room – there's no other explanation. Who in this tiny world actually wants an article by S. Dealler stating that 500,000 cattle infected with BSE will have been eaten by 1997?'

'Keep calm, Steve. You can't be certain that that's where

it's gone, and if you start making a noise about it before you're sure the media will simply ignore you as a nutcase,' he advised.

'I wouldn't mind, you know, if they'd simply asked me for a copy! Why not just ring up and ask for one? Whoever took it probably simply just wanted to know what I was going to say. They must have realised they wouldn't be able to prevent publication.'

'I've been asked to go to see Dr Tyrrell at the Royal Showground,' said Lacey, sensibly changing the subject,' and I've asked them if you can come too. Do you want to? It may just end up with me showing Tyrrell that his advisers from MAFF aren't telling him the full details,' he said. 'But do I know that they think they have more data than we do.'

'I'd love to come. The trouble is that smoke nearly comes out of my ears when I hear some of the things they say. You'll just have to hold me down.'

The Stoneleigh meeting

The meeting took place a few weeks later, in the middle of the summer, at the MAFF pavilion at the Stoneleigh showground. Tyrrell (who did indeed think that we were scientifically misunderstanding the subject), John Wilesmith, the epidemiologist, and Ray Bradley, the man in charge of BSE work at CVL, were expecting to be able to convince Professor Lacey and myself that there would be no risk from BSE to humans. Since I had just calculated, using MAFF's own data, that the risk to humans was unacceptably high, and since I knew that MAFF had carried out similar calculations themselves, I was not impressed. Wilesmith put forward the theory that the cases of BSE born after the feed ban in 1988 were caused by infective tissue continuing to be present in the food on farms. They did not, however, realise that I had carried out a survey of farmers and found that they did not keep feed for more than a month or six weeks, while Lacey had investigated how long it took for the feed to rot due to potentially infective fungi.

According to MAFF, new evidence now showed that only the brain of an infected animal carried any infectivity. They seemed to think we should accept this as sufficient reason to give in and admit that humans were not at risk. It seemed surprising to me at the time that we were expected not to ask how the experiments were done and how much infectivity was needed to produce a positive result in the tissues. I found out later that 3mg of a variety of tissues from an infected cow had been inoculated into the brain of a number of mice. If the mouse died of a TSE, then the test was declared positive. If it did not, then the test was negative and the tissues proclaimed to be not infective. (This time MAFF data on these experiments has claimed that 10mg of tissue was inoculated; this is physically impossible to carry out given the small size of mice and must have included tissue inoculated into the abdomen of the animal. The actual amount inoculated into the brain would have been less than 1mg, and it is this quantity that matters when calculating IU quantities in tissue.)

What they did not seem to realise (although I am convinced that anyone researching in the subject should have done) was that such a small amount was inoculated that there would need to be at least 300 IU per gram of tissue for 50% of the mice to become infected (if 1 IU was needed to infect a mouse). In addition, there had been no control tests and so there was no indication of how many IU were really needed to infect a mouse at all. It was bound to be more than 1 IU, and would probably be between 10 IU and 10,000 IU. If it had been 10,000 IU then 3mg of the tissue must contain 10,000 IU in order for the 50% of mice to be affected. If that was the case, then MAFF's results showed that tissues contained fewer than 300 × 10,000 IU per gram, in other words 3,000,000 IU per gram.

Tyrrell had made it quite clear to us that he would think of beef tissue as a risk to humans if a meal contained more than 10,000 IU; we made it equally clear to him that these experiments were of no help in indicating our meals to be safe by his system. After all, a human meal of 100g (4 oz) of meat might have contained 100 × 3,000,000 IU (100 times the amount that could be in a gram of tissue and yet find the inoculation experiment to be negative) and yet still a mouse inoculated with 3mg might show no signs of disease. As we expected, the MAFF people did not accept this and were convinced that the mouse test was perfect – Tyrrell, however, did seem to understand and said he would put our objections to his committee.

Towards the end of the meeting I started discussing my research and the calculated risks of BSE. Wilesmith did not believe it could be done, so Lacey suggested that I get a copy of the article (which I had laboriously reconstructed from an earlier print-out after the presumed theft) and let Tyrrell at it. It was in the car and I walked over the lawn with John Wilesmith to fetch it, which gave me a chance to explain how the figures had been obtained. I showed him the strange effect of the number of cases reaching a peak at the age of five years and dropping at the age of six and seven, but then starting to rise again by the ages of eight and nine. It was as if there were two peaks, as if there had been two groups infected.

We went back to the MAFF pavilion and I handed Tyrrell the copy. He immediately turned round and handed it to Bradley. I insisted that it was specifically for him, and not for MAFF. He just said that Bradley would send copies to all the members of the Tyrrell Committee; to me, this confirmed that much of the data that the committee members received was in fact vetted by MAFF before they received it. Perhaps it was done to save the members' time, but it certainly happened. I demanded that it should not be given to MAFF and that the information should not reach them before publication. 'Don't worry,' they said, 'it won't go further than us.' John Wilesmith and Ray Bradley drove off together, with Wilesmith studying the paper hard. That was not what I had intended should happen. In the end the paper got through to all the major people in MAFF who might be interested before it reached the rest of the Tyrrell Committee.

Bradley was supposed to give copies of the article to all the members of the committee before the next meeting, which was scheduled for October 1993. Bradley could not send it to them without my permission, he said. As I had given him permission at the Royal Showground, and made it clear that I did not want the article to be shown to anyone outside the committee and this had been ignored, I was peeved. I knew what would happen: MAFF would devote considerable time to trying to think of anything at all that could be wrong with it.

'They'll have a tough time, because it was so conservative all the way through,' I said to Lacey.

'They'll manage it,' he replied.

Politics, chicanery and rejection

I travelled back to York and found the usual pile of letters on my desk. About halfway down was one from the Yorkshire Regional Health Authority, telling me that my contract had been terminated and I was to be out of work in approximately nine months. This may seem a long period of notice, but for a specialist who has spent 12 years in training nine months is actually quite a short time to get retrained! What on earth was happening now?

I rang the Health Authority and asked what had happened. They did not know. I rang the person in charge of my training, who told me what sounded like a lot of nonsense. This was ridiculous. My consultant had not been asked; Lacey, who was in charge of the department had not been asked; I had discussed with the Authority precisely what I was to be doing. I could not get it out of my head that this was not rational but political.

Eventually Bradley sent my work to the committee with at most a couple of weeks to go before the meeting. This was a long and difficult paper, not something to skip through over a cup of tea. Predictably, all that would happen was that I would be accused of being Lacey's poodle and my results would be pronounced unacceptable. By this time, however, the editor of the *British Food Journal* had been sent the article and it was being prepared for publication in November 1993.

A few weeks later I received a very polite letter from Tyrrell, stating that they had decided to take no notice of my article. It had been given a few minutes at the meeting, but the members felt that various factors made the findings invalid. Firstly, he said, they had by this time found that there was no infectivity in any of the tissues of a cow with symptoms except in the brain and spinal cord, and secondly they could not accept my method of calculation of the amount of infection present in food. After all, each meal would contain a relatively small amount, and there was no evidence that infectivity would be cumulative. So Lacey was right again. No matter how conservative I had been in my calculations, they would not be prepared to accept them.

At the time, the 'no infectivity' findings in the tissues of the cow seemed very odd indeed. In all other species infected with a TSE it had been found that the spleen and lymph nodes had been highly infective. From Table 9 it is clear that infectivity is everywhere in differing quantities. Finding that the cow had no infectivity in its spleen had one of two meanings: maybe there really was no infectivity, or maybe the method of looking for it was invalid. As has already been seen, they did not yet know how many IU were needed to infect a mouse, and it seemed much more likely, based on previous trials, that the mouse was difficult to infect with BSE. While that was true (and it is true to any scientist who has worked on TSEs and looks at the results), it was also true that the results of an experiment in cattle to find out how much brain tissue contained an IU, and hence how many IU were needed to infect a mouse, depended on waiting for four years. After all, we would have to inoculate some cows with brain tissue and wait for them to die. At the current time, all we could do was look back at the tissue levels that I had stated in my article. One of the things that stood out prominently was that the MAFF results from mouse inoculation had only been available since about June 1993. Up to that date they should certainly have been assuming the levels of infectivity in the same way that I had; clearly they had not been doing so. The findings with the mice experiments did not seem to change any of their policies – did this mean that they had been assuming very low infectivity levels all the way from 1989?

Tyrrell did not seem to realise that the amount of infectivity that would need to be in tissue for a mouse to become infected at all was quite large (300 IU per gram, because only one three-hundredth of a gram could be injected), even if only 1 IU was actually needed to infect a mouse (which was very unlikely). This meant that in a single meal a human could easily be eating just less than 30,000 IU from a cow tissue when that tissue did not infect mice even by intra-cerebral inoculation. In other words the mouse inoculation test could never, even by showing negative results, indicate that humans were not at risk.

Concerning the 'lack of evidence that TSEs are cumulative', I find that too very strange. The reason that the experiments had not been done in many other species to find out whether this was true was because they were presumed to be so by so many researchers. The TSE agents are not broken down by enzymes and are not excreted in urine; they are taken up by nerves and immune tissue. If that is the case, they will build up just like other chemicals that are not broken down. The incubation period of the disease is very long and there appears to be no chance that an animal will recover, but no immunity to the agent ever seems to build up – no antibodies are produced. All these factors indicate that the body cannot get rid of infectivity and illustrate why researchers assume that it will build up.

The Tyrrell Committee was continuing its previous course of taking the best-case scenario – that all cases would be reported, that infectivity in tissue that was eaten before symptoms appeared would be very low (before or after any experiment to show it), that the mouse inoculation test would be a good indicator of the amount of infectivity in the tissue, that abattoirs would always throw away the offal. It was all very optimistic.

This then becomes a serious ethical question. If one knows that infectivity has been found in tissue of other animals with similar diseases, should one assume infectivity to be in similar tissues of an infected cow? Or should we assume that it is not there from a test that is known to be poorly sensitive? Remembering that this is a fatal disease, with no method of treatment, it becomes clear that by rights we should assume that worst possible scenario. In fact that was what Lacey was doing, and he was being taken to the cleaners by the press for his trouble. That was not what I was doing. I was being as conservative as would be scientifically acceptable – but I was still being ignored by the Tyrrell Committee.

£38,054,040 was paid to farmers in compensation for BSE in 1993.

It was no good simply waiting for the public to complain about the way they were being treated, and it was equally useless asking official groups to stand up and take the flak for their trouble. I was going to have to do some of this myself.

Publication but a low-key response

We obtained 250 copies of my article, 'Bovine Spongiform Encephalopathy: the risk to man', from the *British Food Journal*. I intended to send copies to everyone in Europe and the UK Government who I thought would be able to help: all the MPs who had said in their original election aims that they were interested in human health; all the government bodies that would need to or ought to know; all the press groups that were going to be informed about it; all the veterinary and medical groups that would be likely to produce publications on the subject. With each article went a note which showed how the information should be interpreted. All this went off within a week of publication.

Dealler from Leeds showed that, if the infectivity of bovine tissues was similar to that found in other species; if we only ate meat, liver and kidney; if all symptomatic cases of BSE were reported and diagnosed; if we had never eaten any infective material before the offal ban; and if no cattle became infected after the feed ban, then the risk to humans from BSE was still unacceptably high. *British Food Journal*, November 1993.

There were a few phone calls: 'Steve, your data. How did you arrive at it? How valid is it? What are our risks? How can we act to decrease them?' The journalists were doing their duty. But it was obvious that they were just getting things ready for tomorrow's paper, and my story might take the place of a car crash or a drugs charge. It was all very depressing. By rights this should have been in the headlines. I was actually ready with a press statement to avoid having my telephone jammed, as it had been when the listeria story broke. This time a few people were interested but not enough. The *British Food Journal* was unfortunately not *Nature* or the *British Medical Journal*, whose reputations carry weight with the press.

'Research claims 1 in 10 could be at risk from beef-eating.' This article gave details of the *British Food Journal* article. Newspapers had to deal in straight figures rather than tables of data and James Erlichman had done his best to put these over. He had asked Mr. Taylor, the Government's assistant chief veterinarian, who had merely said that I had gone over the top with my calculations. The fact that we would be likely to eat between 10,000 and 100,000 times as much BSE as scrapie did not seem to be answered. There was virtually no other press response from the article. *Guardian*, 30 October 1994.

I telephoned various people in MAFF. Meldrum, the second most senior person, was willing to talk. He probably saw it as his duty to bring someone like me, who had seen that his results had apparently been ignored, down to earth. Unfortunately it was evident that he had not read the paper properly, even though he had been given a copy by Bradley long before. He talked about transmissible mink encephalopathy (TME) being mentioned in it numerous times, and might have been confusing it with TSE. He said that I should never have included mink muscle tissue levels of infectivity, as they were misleading. I countered that they were not misleading (although they were ten fold too high in my estimation) because I had not included them in risk calculations for humans. He ended up by telling me that he fed his children quite happily on beef and wasn't worried about it. Did he ask his own scientists if they did, I wonder.

Replies of a sort came from many of the MPs, who generally thanked me for the letter and sent it on to MAFF for the standard reply. MAFF was not even re-examining the data. All they had done was instruct someone to reply to my letters.

A letter arrived. It was on unheaded paper, postmarked Weybridge. 'Keep looking for cases of BSE in cattle that have not been fed any infected meal. Maybe there is more to it than just meal. Please destroy this letter.'

This was really quite shocking. The previous anonymous letters I could have worked out for myself, but this one implied that there was data that was simply not getting out. Was it the needles that were used on multiple cattle that passed the disease amongst them in herds where many cases had been reported? Or was it something else? The letter gave no specific information and so was not breaking any laws.

So what is going on at MAFF? Is it that they just don't know enough about the subject? Is it that they are bending over backwards to see a rosy viewpoint? I doubt this, and feel that its staff are probably perfectly honest people who have worked with the agriculture industry for many years. They must have viewed their task as achieving a balance between possible human risk from eating beef and the certain damage to the industry that would take place if consumers saw BSE this way.

The *Guardian* did a short section on the subject, headed 'Dr Dealler predicting millions may die of BSE', but that did not draw forth any response from anyone at the top. Responses from MAFF were so uninformed as to be embarrassing. They did not seem to realise that the prion protein was made from a normal protein of the infected cell and so was structurally determined by the genes of the animal that was infected; so if a disease was passed from one species to another you could not be sure that it would remain infectious to the same range of animals. This was already demonstrated in BSE in that, if it was indeed derived from scrapie, it had already lost its infectivity to hamsters but gained infectivity to cats. MAFF were also convinced that the regulations ensured that all the infective parts of the cow were discarded, and they were even more convinced that all cattle with symptomatic BSE were being destroyed. A quick look at the textbooks would indicate that other parts of the body of an animal infected with a TSE would be infective, and my calculations showed that 85% of infected cattle were being eaten before they exhibited symptoms.

The same replies were being sent by MAFF to the MPs as were being sent to me, and I could see that if I had not known much about the subject they would probably have seemed quite reasonable. It is clear that MAFF were depending on the ignorance of both the media and the politicians to allow their policies through. I went down to the House of Commons to see Gavin Strang, the Opposition front bench spokesman on agriculture. He was obviously worn out, as was I, and was called over to the House halfway through our discussion. I got the impression that he had looked at the article and had gone over it with MAFF officials, who simply explained what nonsense it was – and he had believed them! The problem about spreading doom and gloom, as I was, is that everyone would rather it wasn't true and would therefore much prefer to believe someone who told them just that.

The chance of my findings making any difference were becoming increasingly slim. There was no way that MAFF could be pressured into changing their mind at this stage on an ethical argument. There did not seem to be any way that I could make things happen through official channels. The way that both MAFF's press office and the press themselves had merrily trampled all over Lacey did not leave much hope from that direction. Tyrrell's rely to me –

which did not enquire whether I had already taken his points into account or ask my opinion on whether I felt his committee's conclusion were valid – was so odd that I felt it unlikely that I could effect any change though him. This left very little in the way of open doors.

It is unfortunately a fact of life that you can hope for things to be true until you are blue in the face, but this has more in common with witchcraft than with the mechanism of science. With science you have to look and see what is happening and then compare it with the data that you already have. We all *hope* that BSE is not a risk to humans, but that will not make it a fact.

CHAPTER NINE

Farmers, zookeepers and the voice of ethics

By the summer of 1993 it was becoming clear that some BSE was being passed from cow to calf. MAFF were saying that this was so minor as not to matter. They were determined to believe that virtually all the cattle getting infected ate their nugget of infection and were just unlucky. Although the renderers had been given a few months' warning that the bovine tissue had to be out of the system by 18 July 1993, the reason that the disease had continued, the Ministry asserted, was simply that some farmers still had some uneaten meat and bone meal (MBM) on the farm: this was held to be enough to carry the disease over to calves born after the date of the feed ban.

It was so much in the interests of the renderers to make their product safe that I could hardly believe that they would continue with the unsafe practice of using ruminant tissue in bovine food. One of the problems for MAFF was that, in order to prevent a stampede of consumers away from beef products, they had to give total assurance that beef was safe. In that case, why should the farmers or renderers carry out all this extremely expensive work? It would cost vast sums of money to dispose of the MBM. The later regulations which stipulated that it could not only not be sold in the UK for use in ruminant feed but nowhere else either, and not even for fertiliser, heavily reduced its value and piles of it built up at rendering sites. MAFF simply could not adequately police the addition of protein from MBM to bovine feed and so could not truly give assurances on the safety of beef.

When cases of BSE started to appear in cattle born after the feed ban (BABs) they assumed, therefore, that it was simply because the renderers or farmers were not playing the game. It quickly emerged, however, that it was not just cattle born in the months following the feed ban who were involved, but animals born two years afterwards were as well. This surely could not be due to the feed, as MAFF had gone back to the renderers when BABs started to appear and put pressure on them. It also could not be due to farmers storing feed from before the ban because it just started to rot if it was left for too long. Farmers' barns were not the driest of places and bovine feed cost a lot of money. The idea was to have it delivered regularly and at fairly short intervals. In this way the farmer did not have to tie up money in bags of meal sitting in a barn and slowly going off.

What do farmers think?

I simply could not believe what MAFF was telling us. I decided to carry out two surveys: at the Royal Show at Stoneleigh and at the Yorkshire Show at Harrogate. One was to ask farmers how long they kept their bovine feed that was bagged, and the second was to ask if many of the cases of BSE had had any siblings die of BSE.

I started at Stoneleigh. 'Would you mind if I asked you some questions?' I felt like a sales researcher in the middle of a shopping centre on Saturday. If I told them I was a researcher into BSE they would just walk off, so after a while I started pretending I was doing a survey of how long people kept their meal for cattle and did not mention BSE. This produced some much easier replies. Of the 50 people questioned six kept it for six weeks and the rest said they planned to keep it for a month, with regular deliveries from the manufacturers. It turned out that the producers were very good about this and were actually quite pleased to do it. It saved them storage space and, as long as things went well, it would be a regular supply of income. The most important thing that turned out was that farmers really did not keep the meal for very long – and MAFF would have known this.

Apparently, when MAFF officers went to see farmers with BAB cases and asked them why they had had a BAB they would ask if the farmer could have kept a bag from before the ban. In turn, he would have a good think and try to remember what happened four years ago to that batch of meal. Of course he could not say that he did not keep a bag. That was OK by MAFF, who could then say that there was no evidence that this case could not be due to feed from before the ban. But all MAFF would need to do was to look at the statistics to realise what percentage of the feed the farmers would have had to keep. It was not just 'a bag' – it was going to have to be half the load that was kept for a year. The meal would often have been in 50kg bags and the sheer space it would occupy would have prevented enough being carried over to 1989. It was possible to work out, using MAFF's 'nugget of infection idea', what percentage of bags would be infected. After all, even though MAFF denied it, at least 15% of cattle born on dairy farms in 1987–8 would have developed BSE if allowed to live long enough. Therefore, for a farm of 100 cattle there would only need to be 15 nuggets of infection fed to the calves, who would collectively eat about 500 bags. Therefore, only 3% of bags would have contained a nugget and therefore, if the rate of infection even dropped 90% by 1989, 50 bags would need to have

187

been kept a year in every affected dairy farm (50% of them) in the country. As the rate had not dropped anywhere near that amount, this reasoning was not going to be possible.

The next thing to try was the possibility that the renderers were still putting infected MBM into the bags. I could find no indication of this and the renderers would have known that if the disease continued then their livelihood was very much at risk.

Going to the Zoo

In early 1994 I decided to go to a meeting at Regent's Park Zoo in London, which was aimed at UK pathologists who were worried about the creeping privatisation of NHS laboratories. At lunchtime I went out into the zoo to look at the animals.

Six of the greater kudu had gone down with a TSE over the previous five years. They had become ill quickly and died in a few days, often when quite young. The animals were thought to have become infected from the same feed as was given to cattle, but deaths had continued in kudu born after the feed ban in the same way as they had continued in cattle. The only problem was that I could find no kudu. Their pen was bare, with no plants and just a few bare sticks in the earth. This was strange in that the pens of similar animals, such as oryx or mountain goats, contained all sorts of interesting plants. I asked to see the vets who were known through the articles that they had written about BSE in the various zoo animals, but one was at another zoo and the other could not be found.

One of the lads offered to show me the kudu, and said that the reason they weren't allowed out was that it was too cold and they were restive. We went to a door which led into the internal animal pens – in fact underneath where viewers could look out over the (now empty) external pen. Tall, brown animals with tall horns, the kudu were walking around on the concrete under the low lighting that came from where we were standing. He showed me the door through which they would normally go to the outside, and pointed out the boots and clothing that zoo staff had to change into before entering the pen. He pointed out the cow kudu whose offspring had died of the TSE, and explained that they were worried that she might be infected as well but was not showing symptoms.

'Do you really have to get changed to go in? You're fairly well dressed for that sort of thing anyway, aren't you?' I asked.

'It's not that, it's all this mad cow disease. We have to get dressed up every day and go in to bag up all the kudu turds. Then they're taken away for incineration.'

'Aren't you a bit worried about going in at all?'

'Well, there was a time when I got a lot of blood on me from one of the animals. I was mighty worried about that, I can tell you. But there must be quite a bit of official worry anyway, because when all the kudu have died they're planning to dig up the top foot or so of soil and cart it away. They're afraid it contains the infection itself. They were even talking about concreting over the whole pen.'

He was a pleasant man, and obviously concerned about his animals, but did not realise that MAFF had made it quite clear to all farmers that the risk of the infection being passed from cattle to other species was minimal. No information seems to have reached farmers concerning the risk that BSE might be getting into the soil. When scrapie-free sheep were put on to land formerly grazed by infected flocks in Iceland, the disease returned. In other words it was the environment that contained the scrapie, but whether it was the land, the plants or the water they did not know.

'You must have noticed that there are no plants in the pen,' he said.

I said that I had, and that it seemed odd.

'That was to prevent scratching, I think. They're worried that the disease is passed from one animal to another, possibly just by touching.'

That was not surprising – scrapie could be passed from sheep to goats in that way, from mice to mice, and probably from mink to others. There might also be a possibility that the mule deer at Fort Collins Zoo had passed chronic wasting disease of deer, another TSE, to the Rocky Mountain elk in the pen next door by touch.

'Oh, yes, they're convinced that the disease of the kudu is a risk to humans. If a visitor drops a camera in from the viewing point, we're supposed to incinerate it!'

When I returned to the meeting I spoke to one of the microbiologists there. 'Should they be taking off the top foot of soil from all dairy farms? Should they be pulling out all the bushes? Should they be concreting over fields? Should farmers have to collect every cow turd and have it incinerated? Should I have to get completely changed before and after I walk on a dairy field? It's difficult to tell whether they're going over the top with the kudu disease, or whether they're being too laid back with the farmers.'

'Another finger-crossing exercise from MAFF.'

A letter arrived. It was on unheaded note paper. The postmark was London. 'Ask a few farmers if the cattle with BSE are the siblings of other cattle with BSE. You may be interested in the results. Please destroy this letter.'

This research was something that I had planned to try anyway. Some farms had had so many cases that it should be possible to find out if there was an association between the cases of BSE on a specific farm. Perhaps the person supplying the suggestion had done so already.

> Dealler and Lacey reported a case in which a cow developed BSE but the veterinary officers refused to accept it as such. The cow was born in July 1989, after the feed ban, and had never been fed meal containing MBM. The cow's mother died of BSE and a sibling had died of an encephalopathic disease but this was not confirmed as BSE under histology. *Veterinary Record*, February 1994.

More market research

The Yorkshire Show takes place at Harrogate, about 20 miles north of where I lived in Leeds. This time I decided to play the game as it should be played, and asked the press office if it was OK to go around asking people questions. Everyone is nervous about BSE. They would all rather it went away tomorrow, and nobody wants any more media interference with the price of beef. After a lot of tactful questioning they said they couldn't see anything particularly wrong with the questions I intended to ask.

I had two helpers, each with a copy of a rapidly printed questionnaire supposedly from a farming information group.

'Are we supposed to go around pretending we're not here to find out about BSE cattle's siblings?' asked Lynda.

'There's no pretending about this. All we want is the information. The aim is quite frankly to have a short survey of the number of cattle in herds, the number of cases of BSE, and the number of those cases that are the brother or sister of another case,' I answered. 'The only thing is that if we walk up and ask them about BSE they'll be too nervous to answer. You'll find they simply deny ever having had a case – even though MAFF figures show that around 50% of herds have had one. Remember, this is a show. The farmers are very proud of their cattle, they've spent many years breeding and looking after their beasts, and the last thing they want is some funny information company asking what's bad about their herd.'

'Would it be better not to ask about their herd at all? what about asking about the herd next door, or "Do you know a herd where there has been a case of BSE?"' suggested Marjorie.

'Let's try it,' I said. 'After all, we're not writing down any names or addresses.'

'What are these pots of sweets for?' asked Lynda. 'Is this really a test of their dietary habits?'

'Everyone who answers a question gets a gobstopper on a stick. I've got far too many. Give the rest to the farmers' mates and kids.'

'What are all these questions apart from the ones on BSE?' asked Lynda.

'I have to admit they're merely to give the impression that the questionnaire isn't just about BSE. They're to make sure the farmer is telling the truth and not saying what he thinks we want to hear. They're to make the question about BSE seem relatively unimportant.'

I started in the dairy cow shed and got through to about 50 farmers. Of these, I should think about half were not interested but a lot (and helped a lot by the gobstoppers) were quite happy to answer questions about a 'neighbour' farm. As soon as they realised that I was not about to publish contentious headline-grabbing data they became much more helpful. Some of them wanted to talk about Lacey.

'I'd 'ave 'im strung up, I would!' was a classic description. They also told me things that were, as far as I know completely wrong, such as 'Them there French, they've got more cases of BSE than we 'ave. Why do we 'ave to pay for a disease that got imported from Europe? It ain't fair.'

All I needed to know really was the number of dairy cattle in the herd, the number of cases of BSE and whether or not any were siblings. I found four siblings, and two were found by Lynda and Marjorie. Afterwards I rang up a farmer I knew who had had eight cases and asked him the questions. Yes, two of them were sisters.

When I looked at the data afterwards it was difficult to work out whether or not the number of siblings we had found was the same as would be found randomly in that number of cattle, so I put it to my helper on the statistical side, John Kent. He tapped it into the computer and came out with the answer. 'Yes, there were too many siblings, and yes, that number would not have arisen by accident in 19 out of 20 random findings.' Were the figures really valid? I must admit I would be pleased if someone else repeated the study. There was a reason, somehow, why if one cow went down with BSE its siblings were more likely to do so than others in the herd. Could this be because both had caught the disease from their mother or father?

Ethical backing

There were two major problems in deciding how to handle BSE: the potential risk to humans from eating infected food (which may lead to no human illness whatsoever if we are lucky), and the certainty that, if all necessary action is taken to avoid this, the beef industry would be severely damaged. How could a Ministry of Agriculture take action that was bound to destroy large parts of the beef and dairy industry? (Yet how could a Ministry of Food not do so? They were, of course, the same organisation.) The only way would be if MAFF received specific directions from the House of Commons, with adequate funding to handle the damage. But why would the Government want to do this? A huge tax burden would not go down well with the voters.

There were two channels which I felt could be approached. The first was the EC, which had such a vast budget that it might well be willing to fund the action that might be needed in the UK. The other was the ethical pressure that might be exerted by the Church and the medical professions. (In fact I was wrong, the German Government was much more effective than either.)

On the train on the way back from London in 1993 I met the Bishop of Wakefield. He listened to my problem concerning the ethics of BSE, and about governments espousing short-term BSE strategies that put the population at risk. He told me how to go about getting specific ethical backing through the Church of England, and that is exactly what I did.

Another point is the logic of the ethical problem. Can a risk to humans be countenanced for financial gain? Can a specific risk be taken, which may turn out to be no risk at all, for financial gain? Could this possible risk be ignored for short-term gain? David Braine, lecturer in ethical logic at the University of Aberdeen, told me that if a risk to human lives could be demonstrated as being possible, then ethically it could not be taken when another course of action that did not run this risk was also possible.

The medical logic was clear as a bell on the subject. If you have two doors, one of which might (but might not) have a tiger behind it and was labelled as such, and the other was known to be safe, you must advise your patient to take the safe option if both doors ultimately lead to the same end.

I have now been in touch with numerous ethical groups, who must remain anonymous for personal security, and it is clear that the action being taken by the Government is not in line with the medical ethics. Tyrrell and Southwood's apparent determination to take optimistic scenarios when deciding whether BSE was a risk was clearly unacceptable. BSE might be derived from scrapie (in which case, even though this is invalid, BSE may not be a risk at all), but then again BSE might not be from scrapie, so we could not guess that it was no risk to humans. Infectivity in

194

tissue might be the same as the highest found in other species, or the lowest. Infectivity in food might accumulate to cause infection, or a large enough dose to cause infection might be contained in a single meal. Mice inoculated with the tissues of BSE-infected cattle may well show a good indication of the amount that is there, but then again it might be dramatically (10,000 times) too low because of the species barrier between cattle and mice. At each point the committees seemed to take the most optimistic line. This is not ethically acceptable when a large percentage of the population may be eating BSE in potentially infective doses. Various articles on this subject have now been accepted by the *Ethics Bulletin* and the *Journal of Nursing Ethics*, and have been submitted to the *Journal of Medical Ethics*.

CHAPTER TEN

A government cover-up?

After the article demonstrating the size of the (under-estimated) risk from BSE was published in the *British Food Journal* I received a letter from *Nature* journal asking me, if I produced anything as significant again, to send it to them. I replied that next year, 1994, I would have much better data in that it could be statistically justified, and I started to organise it. What I failed to anticipate was that by the end of October 1994 I would have enough data to show that the risk was much worse than I had anticipated, and that BSE was going to go on for a very long time.

Spongiform Encephalopathy Research Campaign It was evident that funding from MAFF for the research into BSE was going to be slashed in 1994. This was presumably because they were patting themselves on the back at having got through the epidemic without the destruction of the UK beef and dairy industries. Now that it was over, why waste all this research funding? They were neither carrying out the research experiments that needed to be done to find out if humans were at risk of catching BSE, nor were they working on potential treatments or diagnostic techniques.

Predictions among the research groups were that funding was doing to drop from £2.5 million (spread over 3 years from 1991) to one-third of this as of 1994. Yet information was being given to the press about the huge amounts of research funding being put into BSE by MAFF. The figure most commonly quoted in the media was £12 million. At first I believed it, then found that the funding was taken from the MAFF research budget that would have been spent on other things. In other words no extra money was being put into research because of BSE. The next thing was that this figure was to be spread over many years. Then it seemed that it was to include many of MAFF's own costs involved in BSE. By 1994 it became obvious that the funding budget was being progressively shrunk. I heard that funding for various avenues of research had dropped to £800,000, which was to be spread over the next three years. That was barely enough for 10 people.

I decided to set up a BSE research campaign and wrote to experts around the world for their thoughts. It had to be set up as a charity trust and Professor Postlethwaite (a retired microbiologist from Aberdeen University), Dr Anne Maddocks (a retired microbiologist from St Mary's Hospital in London) and Dr Martin Schweiger (an expert in public health from Leeds) volunteered to be members of the trust. I raised £10,000 from various sources and got the Charities Commission to accept the group. All a bit hopeful, but research into BSE must be funded somehow.

Lies, damned lies and statistics?

Again, I knew that all my findings had to be based on MAFF's own data. If they were not then I would quite simply be ignored. Repeatedly that year I contacted John Wilesmith for details of the numbers of cases of BSE in the UK. He would annually put together the age distribution of the cases reported in that year, and each year things appeared to be getting clearer in as much as there were progressively fewer cases where the age of the cow was unknown. This had made it easier each year to be sure of the true number of cases going down in each age group. In February these numbers had been requested from MAFF by Gavin Strang, the Opposition front bench spokesman on agriculture, and he had received accurate and reliable data. Unfortunately I had to wait until after March to get the data directly from John. It cannot have been because the data was not ready. I can only suppose that they did not want me to have it. They knew that I would carry out standard epidemiological maths on the figures and extrapolate from it a lot of data that they would rather not see delivered into the hands of the media.

Heye from Essen in Germany reported a case of CJD in a man who had donated 55 blood units. By the time the man showed his symptoms only nine patients were still alive, the others not having died of CJD. Their survival times were 4, 5, 8, 11, 12, 12, 16, 17, and 20 years. No evidence was found of CJD being transmitted by blood transfusion. *Lancet*, January 1994.

This was as good a study as could be carried out.

Growing tired of waiting, I asked for the figures for the numbers of cases of BSE diagnosed by MAFF in cattle born after the feed ban. Now, the data for this was completely valid. I was sure it had to be because it had already been presented to the EC as indicating that the number of cases was dropping rapidly. This was supposedly as a result of the feed ban, implying that MAFF was absolutely right about the BSE being caused by infected food. Had MAFF not said that a feed ban would cut the disease off rapidly? Here was the proof of just how good their predictions had been.

The first thing you notice when looking at these figures (see Table 19) is that the numbers of affected cattle reported as born in the various years after the feed ban were falling. Indeed, in the figures for 1993 the number of cases reported born in 1988 was dramatically higher than the number of those born in 1990. I could just imagine this being presented to the EC, which would have no reason to doubt this interpretation any more than anyone else who did not know that it was misleading. What was actually needed was not the number 'reported' but the number 'infected'. I went to explain this to Professor Lacey.

'I luv life: tragic diary note of girl doomed by mad cow burger.'

This was a two-page spread in the *Daily Mirror* on 26 January 1994, about Vicky Rimmer, who was dying of a chronic encephalopathy. Her granny, Beryl, was convinced that it had been caused by all the beefburgers she had eaten when she was younger.

Lacey was adamant that this would be just the first.

'Look – in 1993 those cases born in 1988 would be between three and four years old, and the number reported for 1993 represents about 20% of the total number that would die of the disease by the age of ten – by 1999. The cases born in 1989, however, would only be between two and three years old. So the number reported represents only 5% of the total that will die by the age of 10 – by the year 2000'.

'Are you sure of that?' he said.

'I'm as sure as you can be. At least I'm absolutely sure that for every cow that dies aged two there will be a lot more that will die at later ages. These are ordinary statistical techniques. Unless there's a change in the ages at which cattle infected when young will die, these figures can be calculated adequately.'

'So what happened when you calculated the full number of cases born in each year after the feed ban, and included the ones that had not yet shown symptoms – the number "infected"? Is there a drop in the number after the feed ban?'

He had hit the point that mattered.

'Yes, there is. The number does still drop quite rapidly after the feed ban, and total numbers of BAB cases born in each year that will die by the age of 10 does drop, even after statistical assessments.'

'I don't believe this. There's something else. I can see just by looking at the numbers that the disease is being passed from cow to calf. Just look at their data. The fall should really have taken place after 1987, not after this magic feed ban in 1988. The cattle are only fed large amounts of feed during the colder months and after calving. The fall should have taken place earlier but it didn't.' At times Professor Lacey is certain of his instincts. 'The feed delivered to the herds only lasts a few weeks. After that it rots. The farmers know of the diseases that the fungi in the feed will cause. Neither can they afford the money or space to have it delivered at much more than six-weekly intervals – most get it every month.'

'Yes, that agrees with my survey of farmers. Out of 50, only a few took it less frequently than monthly,' I said.

'In that case this marvellous drop should have been appearing earlier, and the number of cases born in the whole of 1988 should have been dramatically lower than that of 1987.'

'At the moment we simply don't have enough data to prove that mathematically. If you stand up and say that to MAFF they will just deny it, as they have with everything else,' I said. 'This is one subject where MAFF researchers have hypnotised themselves into being certain – they've assured everyone that BSE will go away as a result of the feed ban. But at the moment, of course it just can't be stated that BSE isn't going away. My maths, even correcting for MAFF's attempt to mislead the EC, actually agrees that it's dropping – even though it's at a much lower rate than would be expected on their reasoning. By rights, of course, there should have been no cases whatever born in 1990 as none could have been exposed to the disease through their food. There must be another method of transmission, but we just don't know what it is right now.'

' "Safe" beef pledge fails to impress Germans.'

Governments' experts disagree on scientific evidence as 'illegal' threat to ban British imports because of mad cow disease remains.

German officials fear that if the disease is transferred to calves it will never be eradicated. German imports of UK beef only represent 8% of total UK exports, but the fear is that German influence might demand more stringent measures to stop UK exports.

The UK claim of beef safety rests on four points:

1. Sick cattle are destroyed.
2. Specific bovine offals are discarded.
3. BSE is just scrapie and so will not infect humans.
4. The feed ban means that cattle born after it will not be infected.

The Germans just reply:

1. Yes, the sick cattle are destroyed, but what about the ones with no symptoms – six times as many?
2. Yes, certain offals are destroyed, but what about the ones that are not destroyed? These tissues have all been found infective in other species with a TSE.
3. No, this is nonsense. BSE may well not be scrapie anyway, and even if it came from scrapie it will have changed. This argument is unacceptable.
4. We wish that was true but already 7,500 cattle born after the ban have developed it. And there may be vertical transmission (cow to calf) indefinitely. *Guardian*, 9 March 1994.

Moving the goalposts

I went away thinking over what he had said, and wondering how we could actually find out why the number of infected cattle born in the years after the feed ban was falling but not very fast. I picked up the disc containing the results that Wilesmith had given me for the number of cases in 1992 of cattle born after the ban, and pushed it into the computer. As the figures came up on the screen I stared at them and thought hard. It took five minutes before something hit me. The number of cases from 1992 could actually be used to predict the number expected for 1993.

Purdey, a farmer from Taunton, put forward the idea that organophosphorous pesticides (OPs) might be involved in the cause of BSE. He suggested that the OPs used to deal with warble fly in cattle might alter the production of the prion protein in its correct form by the brain. The magnesium-induced prolonged remission in the disease was possibly due to its action on cellular interaction.

He also reported BSE in a two-and-a-half-year-old daughter of a BSE cow. The daughter had not, however, received any animal-based proteins and was only one month post-conception upon arrival on the farm. *Journal of Nutritional Medicine*, 1994.

It is just like an experiment with other diseases. Imagine that you inoculated 100 children with a vaccine and waited to see if any of them became immune. Some would do so after six days, some seven, some eight, some nine, some ten and few after that. Suppose you did this experiment a few times, got the same results, and then decided to do just two more of them. In the first of these, the headteacher decided to take 33 children away to another school after three days. The result would be exactly the same, but each of the numbers showing immunity on days 6 to 10 would be just one-third lower. You could easily calculate the number that would have shown immunity had all of them stayed at the school.

When the experiment was done for the last time, however, imagine you had lost the date on which the inoculation had taken place and you could not remember how many children had been transferred to another school. All you knew was that on the first day in which any immunity appeared eight children did so, and 16 on the second day. From those two figures, taken in conjunction with the results of your previous experiments, you could work out all the details. You could find out when they were inoculated (because this was six days before the first immunity appeared), you could tell how many had been transferred (because if none were transferred there would have been 10 on the first day; there were only 8, so one fifth were taken away). You could even predict the numbers that were going to show immunity on each of the following days!

Alperovitch in France reported that CJD was similar in prevalence in cases per million of the population in France, Germany, Italy, the Netherlands and the UK. *Lancet*, April 1994.

The BAB cattle were much the same (see Table 16). We had the figures for the proportion of cattle which would die in all the different age groups, so if we knew how many had died aged three for any particular group of cattle we must be able to calculate the number that would die in the following year. I quickly calculated, from the groups of BAB cases born in 1988 and reported in 1992, the number that should be reported in 1993. The 1993 case numbers that had actually been reported to MAFF were in my briefcase.

The numbers reported turned out to be dramatically lower than those predicted in my calculations. Some factor must therefore have changed between the pre-ban and post-ban years. Maybe the cattle were no longer eating infected material and so were not becoming infected. No, that was not the answer. The vast majority of cattle born before the ban were only fed infectivity in that year or for two years at the most, and then had none in their diet for the rest of their lives. In fact cattle being born in years leading up to the feed ban lived in fewer and fewer years before the ban (a cow born in 1986, for instance, would live two years before the ban, whereas one born in 1987 would only live one). This appeared to make no difference in the age distribution of the subsequent cases of BSE in these groups. Also, the MAFF's 'nugget of infection' theory, in which a cow ate the BSE-poisoned nugget from a batch of food, would mean that a young cow would be very unlikely to eat more than one nugget anyway. No, the age distribution of cattle reported with BSE was remarkably steady and did not vary with the feed ban. It was quite remarkable, and I shall return to this topic later.

Ye in New York found that the cells involved in making insulin change in size and number in hamsters infected with scrapie. *Journal of Comparative Pathology,* 1994.

Carp had shown in 1989 that scrapie induced obesity in mice as a result of changing the way insulin dealt with sugar. Could this be one of the first things we shall see if BSE infects humans?

Perhaps the number of BAB cases reported in 1993 was low because there had been a change in the way in which cattle were chosen for slaughter. Maybe far more dairy cattle were being slaughtered than previously? I looked into these and found minimal changes – certainly not the 40% variation that would have been required to explain the low number of reported BABs. Dairy herd numbers were dropping steadily but not by much, according to MAFF data.

I was seeing here a 40% drop in the number of cases that could simply not be due to any feed ban. There was no connection between the feed ban and changes in slaughter policy, and without that there would be no way in which the steady age distribution of cases should change in such a dramatic way. If the feed ban was such an important factor then cattle born before the feed ban, and fed no more infection after their first birthday (for instance), would also show a decrease in case numbers.

A letter arrived. It was on unheaded paper. The postmark was (?) Weybridge. 'We have not heard from you for some time. Don't stop. You are one of the people whose science they are actually afraid of. They will cut the funding for internal research unless the media and the outside world keep at them. Remember to look into what is actually wrong with the histology-negative cases. Destroy this letter.'

A month earlier I had given a talk in Wetherby in Yorkshire. A local vet had stood up at the end and said that, as soon as MAFF changed some rules concerning their acceptance of cases of BSE for compensation, he found the number of cases of BSE in cattle born after the food ban just dropped. When he had asked the farmers what had happened they told him that they just weren't reporting them because 'it just wasn't worth it.'

That was it. The huge difference between predicted case numbers and reported ones was due to MAFF data not having any indication of the proportion of clinical cases still being reported. I wrote to John Wilesmith and demanded further data. 'You must realise what this means?' I said in the letter. I received no reply.

Lacey and Dealler from Leeds suggested that BSE might be transferred vertically, from cow to calf. They showed that this had happened with other prion diseases and said we should not assume that it would not happen regularly with BSE. *Human Reproduction*, 1994.

This was looking very grim. MAFF were unwilling to provide data, or to reply to letters. I rang up a contact at CVL.

'Have they noticed that the figures for BAB cases reported in 1993 are far too low?' I asked.

'Yes, they have.'

'Well, have they put forward any ideas about what could be causing the drop?

'At the moment it's just being treated as a strange phenomenon, and they're trying to put it down to the lack of post-ban infection. It simply won't fit, of course, but they don't know how to explain it.'

'They must know that the same factors also apply to the cattle born before the ban, though – they too haven't been fed any infectivity since the ban. It would almost seem that the incubation period in the cattle born after the ban was simply much lower than in those born before it. If anything, it should be the other way around – the BAB cattle should be eating less infectivity and then living for longer.'

'They would much rather it just went away you know. Even if you can drag out some data to prove what you're suggesting, I'm sure they would just deny it.'

'Time bomb over infected blood.' Health Minister Thomas Sackville has been forced to admit that of the 156 cases of CJD reported since 1990, 22 'are believed to have given blood at some stage'.

David Hinchliffe MP got this answer in a reply from a Parliamentary Question concerning 60-year-old Marie Walkden, who died from suspected CJD that her relatives believe she caught from blood transfusions.

Mr Sackville says there is no medical evidence that CJD can be passed on by blood transfusion.

Richard Lacey of Leeds University, Britain's leading expert on CJD and BSE, says: 'Mr Sackville is misinformed. In Australia it has been proved that at least four people have died from receiving transfusions of CJD-infected blood.'

Significantly, the Department of Health has now banned everyone suspected of having CJD from giving blood. Lacey believes that CJD is mainly caused by people eating beef from cattle infected with BSE, although the Government has always claimed there is no proven link. *The People*, 25 May 1994.

Government policy on BSE and specified bovine offals (sent to all directors of public health by computer link on 20 June 1994). This was a Parliamentary Question answered by Agriculture Minister Gillian Shephard.

'The Government's Chief Medical Officer continues to advise that there is no evidence that humans can contract CJD from an animal in the UK over the years 1985 to 1993. Also the Chief Veterinary Officer advises that the incidence of BSE among cattle in the UK continues to fall as a result of the sharp decline in the incidence of the disease in cattle less than five years old.'

Results had been found, however . . .

'These results show that it is possible to transmit BSE to laboratory mice from intestines taken from young cattle when fed a substantial dose of brain material known to contain BSE. It is not surprising that BSE has been found in these tissues, which scientists have always considered a likely route for feed-borne infection. The relatively short period in which the infectivity has shown up, in one case six months after being fed the BSE dose, does, however, raise the issue of whether calves up to six months should continue to be exempt from the ban on the use of specified bovine offals (SBOs), of which the intestine is one.'

This was followed by a ban on the use of intestines and thymus from calves under six months of age for human food.

The Government did not actually admit that the Tyrrell Committee had been wrong in permitting these tissues to have been eaten for the previous four and a half years. It also did not ban the eating of other offals such as spleen and tonsils, which are also likely to be infected. It is not clear why the Tyrrell Committee did not recommend this, as it is known from mouse experiments that the spleen becomes infective very early.

The Government also did not advise any of its European partners to do the same with the gut and thymus of the calves that were exported to be raised as veal on the continent.

Sometimes I think I am finding new factors, but I am on my own with a PC and minimal data. The boys at the CVL actually have paid statisticians and three full-time researchers; of course they must have known. Presumably they would rather it was not true, and must be hoping I cannot prove it statistically.

'Beef deal still possible as Germans vote for ban'. The German Parliament's upper house, the Bundesrat, voted to back a unilateral decree empowering the German Government to enforce a six-month partial ban on bovine imports from the UK. The EC said it would take Germany to the European Court of Justice for breaking free-trade rules if Bonn signs the ban. Because of this Helmut Kohl and John Major were to talk at the end of a meeting in Naples.

Yesterday Gillian Shephard, the Agriculture Minister, threatened action against Germany through the European Court. 'I am disappointed by the Bundesrat decision but I am hardly surprised, as Germany has persistently ignored the science on BSE and shows willingness to step outside community law'.   *Guardian*, 9 July 1994.

It's already too late

The results that I had come up with from the BAB data were simply so glaring that I was convinced they could be justified statistically. I took them to a statistician neighbour of mine who put me on to Professor Kent in the statistics department at Leeds University. I gave him a lot of data and let him chew over it.

When he went through it he found that under-reporting (or some other way in which the number of reported clinical cases in MAFF's data was lower than the true number) was demonstrable not only when calculated by the method that I had carried out, but also by another much more precise method.

'We simply have to assume that in some of the years the

number of cases reported was a good representation of the number that really were appearing in British farms,' he said.

'Well, that would have to be 1990 or 1991,' I replied, 'because earlier than that the vets and farmers hadn't really got into the habit of looking for cases (and weren't being compensated with much money if they found any), and after 1991 I'm not satisfied that farmers were being encouraged by MAFF to report cases at all. Does that make sense with the maths?' I replied, getting ready for John to blow my mind away with numbers.

'Yes, that makes the most sense. After all a farmer can't report more cases of BSE than there actually are – he has to have the carcass to prove it. The years 1990 and 1991 are the ones in which the apparently highest proportion of cases were reported.' He was obviously sure of his data. 'We can now produce good figures for the proportion of cases that would die in each age group. In fact we can even calculate just how certain we are that these figures are correct.'

'So why have MAFF not done this themselves?' I asked, expecting him to tell me that he was not sure or that it was simple.

'I'd actually be quite surprised if they could do this one. It's heavy stuff and might be a surprise to them as well.'

So MAFF might not be concealing their figures – they might just not have top-notch statisticians.

'Can we now calculate the levels of under-reporting?' I asked. 'That's what's needed in the end.'

John pulled out the data and spread it on the table in front of me. He went through the figures and calculation methods one at a time. This took an evening a week for three months. At the end it was clear that there had been gross under-reporting in 1992 and 1993 and, taking into account John Wilesmith's original epidemiological study of BSE in 1987–8, it was clear that specific conclusions could be drawn and that there would be adequate data to be sure of them.

What the data revealed

Eight major conclusions could be drawn.

1.   When MAFF's data for the number of cases of BSE that were reported in all the years from 1989 to 1993 were simply written down in such a way that the cows born in different years were followed, it became clear that there was a *peak in the incidence of cases aged five* (see Table 17). It was now also possible to calculate the proportion of cattle that would die of BSE at different ages (see Table 18).

2.   Out of the five years for which we had figures, *apparent under-reporting was present in 1989, 1992 and 1993*. One of the things that stuck out a mile was that the under-reporting only seemed to be in the cattle born after the feed ban. In other words, cattle born before the ban were being reported normally in 1992 and 1993, and predictions for them turned out to be accurate. It was the BABs that tailed off oddly in those years.

3.   The obvious fact that came from this was that the *occurrence of BSE rose in a logarithmic curve (rising faster and faster) until those born in 1988 and then dropped slowly*. Unfortunately the statistical certainties were too wide to be sure that it was dropping at all after that date. In other words at this time we cannot say that the feed ban caused any drop in the number of cases born in the following years (see Table 19).

4.   Wilesmith's data in 1989 showed that there must have been a method by which the disease passed from one farm to another. He noted that the disease did not spread out from a single site but spread rapidly into many parts of the country. This was called *horizontal transmission* – one cow infected another through recycling of bovine tissue in

MBM. He decided that there was no evidence of *vertical transmission* (mother infecting calf) or familial associations (cattle of the same breed or closely related being much more likely to develop BSE than others). But what had I found? The picture we now had was exactly what would be expected from vertical transmission.

So where did the truth lie? There was definitely some mode of horizontal transmission, but was it necessarily the MBM? Then again, the feed ban really did appear to have an effect. After all, the number of cases would have been expected to rise again in 1989 if the ban had had no effect.

As far as I was concerned, I needed to look no further; it was clear to me that Lacey had been absolutely correct. The cases of BSE that we now see are the *offspring* of the cattle that became infected from the feed. The mothers may well be destined to become symptomatic later in life, but they are only allowed about 25% of their natural life expectancy before they are slaughtered. I decided the next step was to calculate how fast we would expect the numbers of BSE cases born in different years after the ban to drop, as the mothers that had been infected before the feed ban were gradually slaughtered after it (see Table 28).

I explained what I had found so far to Professor Lacey and went on to the later statistics. 'We now know that about 25% of the offspring born of UK dairy cattle in 1988 would die of BSE if allowed to live long enough. Therefore, it must be that as cows only have one calf per year, at least 25% of the mothers are infected also.'

'Or perhaps all the cows are infected and only 25% of their offspring are catching it from them,' he suggested.

'Or again, the truth could be somewhere in between. Only a proportion are infected and only a percentage of the calves catch BSE.'

'Is there any way to find out where the truth lies?' he asked. 'What we really need to know is how many cattle are infected. Without that we can't work out the number of infected animals we are eating.'

'The first step is to work out how fast the number of cases would drop in cattle born after the ban in each of the possibilities,' I said. 'The one that fits best is that all the cattle of the herd are infected and 25% of their offspring catch the disease [see Table 28]. That means that by the year 2001, assuming that no cattle born after 1991 ever became infected (even though we now know that the cases will really go on well into the next century), we will have eaten around 1,800,000 infected cattle that would otherwise have died of BSE if permitted to live until the age of 10, and a further 8 million mother cattle which, having been infected later in life, may never show any sign of disease by the age of 10.'

'That's an awful lot. I presume you've done as before and taken underestimates at every turn? Did you assume that there would be no disease passed from the infected calves to their offspring?'

'Yes. If the disease becomes endemic and starts to be passed on from one generation to another, the figures will be bigger again. But then again, if we really do see only 25% of the offspring of infected cattle becoming infected themselves, then it won't become endemic. There just isn't enough certainty at the moment to be sure of this, however. All we can say is that the disease will still be in the UK well into the next century.'

'A disaster,' he said. 'Stephen, why does MAFF see what it wants to instead of looking at this scientifically?'

5. *The risk to humans is unacceptably high* or at least should be assumed to be so at this time. When I calculated the risk figures using the new 1993 data, taking under-reporting into account, the results were higher than those found for 1992, showing millions of people having eaten a potentially fatal dose of BSE in 15 out of 21 possible outcomes (see Tables 29 and 30).

6.   *It is already too late for adults in Britain to stop eating beef* in order to decrease any individual non-vegetarian's risk. There has to be a tenfold difference in the level of infectivity in the inoculum (or presumably the amount of food) taken into an animal to alter dramatically the risk of developing a TSE. In other words if we ate twice as many infected sausages we might increase our risk of developing BSE but not by much, whereas if we ate ten times the number the risk would be clearly increased. It appears that 1994 was the peak year for BSE cases and 1993–4 the peak time for infectivity in our food. If we cross our fingers and hope that the disease does not become endemic we will already have eaten half the infective agent that we can potentially eat throughout the epidemic. Put another way, if we stop now we can only halve the amount we would eat in total. This drop is just not enough to make a big difference to our risk. The only things that would alter human risk now are:

(a) Stopping the feeding of beef and beef products to children or, at least, slaughtering older cattle.

(b) Stopping the export of beef from the UK.

(c) Warning people visiting the UK not to eat any beef products.

(d) Research into methods of treatment, diagnosis and prevention.

I presented these results to a research company and the people round the table almost audibly gulped.

'You cannot put that out to the media,' one said.

'I can. In fact ethically I ought to. It's the Government that can't.'

'Can you imagine what effect that would have? If I was on a tourist plane to the UK and I got a piece of paper from the captain warning me not to eat any beef or I might die, I don't think I'd get off.'

'Oh, I don't know. I don't think this sort of warning is so dreadful – after all, lots of places warn you not to drink the water, but you still go. No, it's the political tarnish after having told everyone that BSE was not a risk that's the real barrier to getting anything done.'

7.   The reason why the number of BSE-infected cattle born in 1988 was already starting to level off before it reached its peak was because *the disease was actually running out of uninfected cattle to infect*.

Gradually, as the disease progressed, the percentage of the dairy herds in the UK that had had a case of BSE rose to about 56%. This is, however, a misleading figure in terms of overall numbers, as it tended to be the largest herds that had cases of BSE and the smaller ones that appeared to remain free of it. The reason must have been partly because such a low percentage of cattle *apparently* became infected that if you only had 20 cows on your farm, it was quite likely that you might never see a case. When the percentage of dairy cattle in the UK that are in an infected herd is calculated the figure rises to over 85%. If, again, you acknowledge that most of the mothers (dams) will be infected in any affected herd, it becomes clear that by 1988 there were few dams left to become infected.

At this point the demand made by Lacey in 1991 that infected herds should be slaughtered has to be re-examined. In fact it was already too late even in 1988 when the feed ban was introduced. MAFF had missed the boat. To have made a dramatic difference in the number of cattle becoming infected, slaughter should have taken place in 1987 or earlier – at which time, of course, neither MAFF nor anyone else could have known which herds were infected. By 1991 slaughter might only prevent BSE from becoming endemic and decrease, but not prevent, the risk to humans.

8.   There appears to be an *environmental factor*, present to a greater extent in one part of the year, involved with the transmission of BSE to young cattle. This can be seen from the months in the year in which the cattle that

die of BSE are born – mostly September and October. This is not initially clear, in that a large number of calves are born at this time anyway. Unfortunately for the age-old spring and autumn calving periods, milk is produced especially after calving. If you want stable milk production from a farm all year round there simply has to be calving all year as well. Artificial insemination takes care of this, and the reason for the big autumn birth peak for cattle that will develop BSE is uncertain. The peak is indeed so high that around half the cattle born on UK dairy farms in this period would be infected. (See Table 32.)

After all the statistics had been done I gave a lecture on the subject which put over much of the same data.

'Dr Dealler, you sound awfully sure of your findings,' said a member of the audience. 'Are there no specific things that would come over a little more easily to us to indicate that you are right? After all, we are not all statisticians.'

'Yes, I'm absolutely sure. But then so are the people at MAFF. In fact John Wilesmith has now published things which say he would put his job on the line if he was wrong. All my data shows is that MAFF's own figures indicate that there may have been gross under-reporting of BSE cases, and that when this is taken into account the scenario that best fits the data is that vertical transmission of BSE is the route by which the cases we now see become infected,' I said. 'There are, however, some further factors that are plain to everyone including MAFF, which should have made them realise the problems themselves.'

'The first is something called the in-herd BSE rate. This is the annual number of cattle developing BSE per 100 cattle on the farm in infected herds. John Wilesmith's data shows that this has remained virtually stationary throughout the epidemic. In other words, once a herd becomes infected it produces the same small number of cases every year. It also means that the huge rise in case numbers is due to ever-greater numbers of herds being infected. I can't describe to you just how strange that is. Why shouldn't case numbers on every farm rise in the same way as the number throughout the country? Surely, if a growing number of "nuggets of infection" are to be found randomly in every hundred bags of meal leading up to 1988, then the number of cases per herd should rise in the same way as the number of cases in the country.

'The reason is simply that *all* the dams in an infected herd are already infected, so you cannot infect any more of them with another batch of infected meal. So the in-herd rate remains steady. The lives of these infected dams, however, will probably end artificially before the disease shows. What happens is that only *some* of the offspring become infected every year from their mothers; but there's no reason why this number should increase as the epidemic progresses. Farms have not seen epidemics of BSE but the country has, and that, I would suggest, is the reason. Does that make any sense?'

A letter arrived. It was on unheaded paper. The postmark was London. 'Keep going at the fall in BSE reporting by farmers. You may find that it is not due to a drop in BSE. Please destroy this letter.'

'Yes, though it really is rather odd,' said a woman in the audience.

'Another very curious factor is that the age distribution of cases of BSE has apparently remained stationary all the way through. If BSE came from sheep we would expect the first cases to have long incubation periods, as is normal when a TSE crosses the species barrier. If infected tissue from these cattle was then fed to other cows, these would be expected to have a shorter incubation period, and this would be expected to become progressively shorter as the epidemic went on. Why is it that the age distribution remains so stationary? What fits very well is that the cattle we see with BSE got a dose of the disease from their mother, and as soon as you realise that, it becomes clear that there is no reason for any change in the age distribution, because all these (second generation) cattle have always been infected in the same way.'

MAFF news release: new beef trade certification discussed 11 August 1994.

The Minister, Mr Waldegrave, met the leaders of the farming and meat industries and agreed some major changes:

1. MAFF is now able to supplement the existing service of checking cattle ear tags to provide information on whether the cow had come from a herd free of BSE within six years.
2. Arrangements would be made to allow freedom of information about BSE to be passed to the veterinary surgeon on the meat plant.
3. A cattle passport would be introduced so that buyers and sellers would know if an animal that was bought or sold was always from a BSE-free herd. This was to be voluntary.

'You must forgive us, Dr Dealler, but we've been told continually by MAFF that BSE comes from the MBM feed. Are there any other of their articles of faith that you would like to destroy?' This from a young woman at the back of the hall.

'Well I could worry about the idea that BSE comes from scrapie.' She nodded. 'That's fairly certain, isn't it?'

'Easing of BSE rules urged as exports plummet 90%.' Exports fell dramatically: 80% of the trade had been in carcass form and about two-thirds of this was of meat from cattle at the end of their milking life. Mr Scott, general secretary of the Federation of Fresh Meat Wholesalers, said that they were looking for places to sell meat off-the-bone to which the six-year certificate did not apply. The farmer now has to obtain certificates to show that the cow has never been on a farm where there has been any BSE – quite a task as cattle may pass through two or three farms via the livestock market. *The Times*, 12 August 1994.

'Remember, when BSE appeared the UK was one of the major researchers into scrapie, but there was no data available on how many cases there were. It seemed a reasonable source for BSE, and I think that at the time it was a perfectly rational hypothesis. After all, they felt that scrapie was increasing, and so apparently was the number of sheep. Since then, however, a number of experiments have been tried. The first involved looking in the brain of the cow for the areas where the disease was present; it was found to be in different areas than scrapie. For some reason this normally seems to remain fairly steady in TSEs, and indeed cats and kudu showed the same distribution of disease as in BSE.

'The next move,' I continued, 'was by the Americans, who inoculated some cows with scrapie to see what happened. They all developed a TSE but in none was it BSE, even if a number of different strains of scrapie were used. In the UK we had inoculated BSE into sheep; again none developed classical scrapie, but they did get a spongiform encephalopathy. My data shows the disease to have started in cattle born in 1979 or 1980. Remember, these may well have been the offspring of infected dams. If the change in the method of manufacture of MBM was involved, then the scrapie that infected the first cow would only have taken hold about 1980. There would then have been time for this mother to have incubated the disease before passing it to her offspring. It seems difficult to fit all this in with the change in MBM production, as it might have had to be 1977 when this first dam became infected. We now know that there was in fact only a minor increase in the sheep population and no evidence has appeared for any increase in scrapie. We all know that sheep are fed some meal, particularly in the winter, and, although the amounts they get are small compared with those received by dairy cattle there should surely have been an epidemic of scrapie too during this period. As far as I know, nobody is pretending that there has been one, and MAFF figures for scrapie incidence for the past two years have been steady. I think that in the early days the scrapie hypothesis was fairly reasonable, but it's simply run out of steam. If we want the MBM manufacturing hypothesis to hold water at all, we may have to drop the idea of scrapie as a source of BSE.'

'German beef boycott backfires.' It was clear that the German action against British beef was determined and the German press had put a large amount of data on to the front pages, including some of my figures.

Butchers had started to put signs up in their windows that no British beef was in their shop, and major supermarkets had refused to buy any more. However, the risk from UK beef was only part of the problem as the customers also stopped eating beef from Germany. A poll for *Die Woche* found that 47% of consumers said they were afraid when buying meat and had changed their habits; 71% said they were afraid of beef.   *Sunday Times*, 28 August 1994.

'Surely it could just have been a particular strain of scrapie?'

'Indeed it could, and I don't think that at this point we can state that scrapie wasn't the cause. One thing I think we must accept now is that, if scrapie was the cause, it would be an uncommon strain of the disease. This means we can't even think of assuming that as scrapie didn't infect humans neither will BSE – which to my mind is a fairly weak argument anyway.'

'Excuse me, Dr Dealler. Did you say that supposition was untenable? That's surely been one of MAFF's firmest arguments all the way through the epidemic?' This came from a bearded middle-aged man at the front.

'I have to admit that I've heard this argument so often that my heart sinks every time I hear it again. How MAFF could have used it in the first place isn't clear. They always knew that the prion protein was derived from the genes of the infected animal. Maybe the infective agent has some DNA or RNA associated with it, but as yet nobody has found it. When a TSE is passed from one animal species to another we see that the range of animals it will infect changes with the transition. For instance, scrapie will infect hamsters but not cats; and if BSE was scrapie and nothing changed when it changed the host animal, we would expect the same to be true for BSE. However, the reverse is true of BSE; it seems to infect cats but not hamsters. Even if BSE came from scrapie, the change in the prion protein that makes up much of the agent being derived from the genes of the host species means that you simply could not safely assume BSE must infect the same animals as scrapie does. This argument of MAFF is to my mind invalid, and I can only assume that they have been using it for political reasons.'

Wilesmith from CVL produced one of the most important epidemiological publications. It showed how the numbers of cases had risen dramatically since 1986, with various winter/spring peaks each year. It also showed that the number of cases of cattle born after the feed ban was building up, but currently were mainly in the short period after the feed ban was introduced.

One of the most important findings was that the in-herd rate of BSE was only minimally changing. During the period that we were watching the national rate rise rapidly, it stayed the same. The reason that the BSE numbers were rising was because more and more herds were becoming infected. *Seminars in Virology*, 1994.

This virtually ruled out the possibility that cattle were becoming infected by just being unlucky in getting the nugget of infection that was randomly in their meal.

'Mad cow disease in Germany's own herds.' There have been reports of a BSE-like disease in Germany and the accusations come after police raided one of the country's slaughterhouses. The source could have been the British cattle feed which was banned in the UK in 1988 and just exported instead. Margrit Herbst, a research vet who works at the Creutzfeld Institute in Kiel, said, 'I estimate that from the animals I see around one in every thousand is infected. I can only talk for north Germany, but I have documents which prove my assertion.' Herbst says that since making her claims she has received telephone threats at her home and has been told by the Kiel state prosecutor's office not to make further statements. The prosecutor's office officials raided the Norddeutsche Fleischzentrale slaughterhouse in Bad Bramstedt, one of the largest in Schleswig-Holstein. The figures supplied by the Germany Embassy suggest that British bone meal exports to Germany fell from 594 tons in 1988 to 9.1 tons in 1990, before being banned this year. *Sunday Telegraph*, 25 September 1994.

The UK Government had told Europe that very little of the MBM had been exported from the UK to the EC anyway and most of it went to the third world.

'You seem to see MAFF as nothing but the bad guys. Surely that can't be true?'

'No, quite the reverse. I see MAFF as fighting for the best deal for the farmers at every turn. The building up of the beef industry after the war has been one of the Ministry's greatest feats. I see MAFF as fighting to preserve it. The only thing, I'm afraid, is that it should not also continue to call itself the Ministry of Food, because if it does, the good of the population should come first and not that of the industry. The whole thing is sad. It may mean the destruction of a major industry, but if this is due to a fatal, untreatable disease that may be a major risk to people it should be done. The heroes of the day are actually the farmers, who should by rights have been fully compensated for a disease which may well have been due to a change in MBM manufacturing processes directed by MAFF. They've taken the brunt of the disease and it's cost them a lot. Let's just hope that we haven't exported BSE to Europe, that we've put the brakes on the disease in Britain, and that humans will be naturally immune.'

To me, the most depressing of all my findings was that it was too late to stop eating beef products in the UK and yet nobody at the meeting had followed this up with questions.

A letter arrived. It was on unheaded paper. I did not write down its source. 'Remember that there have been a number of farms with a lot of BSE. They have investigated them and not found a specific association with meal. MAFF's investigation of Narang's work should be reviewed. Please destroy this letter.'

CHAPTER ELEVEN

How can we make them listen?

My position as a senior registrar in York was becoming more and more tenuous. I had been given several months to pack up my bags and look for another specialisation when I was offered a locum job in Burnley. As a locum you are only looking after the post until they find the right person to do it permanently, and your job is to get on with everyone and not to rock the boat.

The news people soon caught up with me, however. MAFF had taken a pounding from the press in 1992 and now they wanted someone else to get their data from. The media had been the heroes in the food world and I felt I just had to help them whenever I could. Within three days of my arrival a TV team from BBC Leeds turned up to interview me. This was not going to look good if I was to fight for the permanent post here.

Putting the message across via the media

The work with John Kent had revolutionised what we knew about BSE and somehow it had to come out. It had been sitting on the desk of the editor at *Nature* for several months and eventually was turned down with a statement that the data was fine but it should be published in a veterinary journal. It was never going to be accepted in one of those. It seemed that the scientific veterinary press was also under MAFF pressure. The next possibility was the *British Food Journal*, an excellent publication that produces top-quality reviews of diet and food processes. It took several weeks to rewrite the data in the format that the *BFJ* wanted, but the article was soon with the editors and was expected to be out by August 1995.

Isabel Tang from Granada TV in Manchester came to see me about the 'new data' on BSE that had been produced. I explained that my data showing that we were eating infected cattle really could not be open to argument because of the enormous number of animals in the UK.

The Institute of Actuaries and the Association of British Insurers became aware that a risk had been taken with the UK population. Initially they did not seem to believe what they were being told, basically by Lacey and myself, so I went to the various groups in London to explain how the research had been carried out. It was at first felt to be a risk that the insurance world could handle, but they soon realised that the people dying of CJD as a result of BSE would be middle-aged and extremely expensive to insure. Independent actuarial assessment was to take place.   July 1995.

'No, Steve. That's simply not going to be good enough for *World in Action*,' she insisted. 'People just cannot understand heavy statistics. They will need to see with their own eyes the proof that you are right.'

'That's not going to be possible,' I replied. 'You would need to take the tissue from the cattle you are testing and inoculate it into other cattle. That's the most sensitive method of diagnosis and you won't be able to do anything like that in the time available.'

'Is there nothing that's any use?'

'There's Harash Narang's experiment.' I told her about Harash, and how he had been pushed around by the Public Health Laboratory Service. 'There's definitely something going on behind the scenes there.'

'Tell me about his test. Is it any good? How long would it take?'

'What we found was that fine fragments of some infected tissue would stick to the surface of an electron microscopy grid and could be stained using standard procedures. He said he could identify infected brain tissue in minutes. The problem is that it's not at all clear if his work is valid. He just seems to be able to repeat it regularly. Maybe we could get hold of the samples of brain and let him test them – but MAFF would pour cold water on the results.'

In July 1995 I visited groups at the Haemophilia Society and their experts at the Hammersmith Hospital concerning the potential risk that blood transfusions and possibly blood clotting extracts would be infected with CJD.

'I'm worried,' said Isabel. 'If MAFF did that we would look complete fools. Isn't there anything else we can try that will produce a result quickly?'

The number of BSE cases confirmed in 1993 was 36,272 and in 1994 it was 25,579. This was proclaimed as a dramatic drop by MAFF. No attempt was made to assess the proportion reported. August 1995.

'We could look for the PrP in the brain using some standard techniques,' I said, 'but the tests are simply so insensitive that, whatever we found, it would be a much lower number than the true figure. I'd be extremely fed up if we did all these tests, found them to be negative, and the media used it to indicate that we were not eating infected cattle – because that would simply not be true. If one of the tests is positive then there can be no argument; the cow was infected. But if the test is negative this means nothing and can't be interpreted unless the sensitivity of the test is certain.'

Jonathan Aitken had not long since accused Granada TV of misinforming the public and putting over libellous statements concerning his alleged relationship with an arms company. He was now a powerful figure in the Treasury and Isabel had to be careful. Journalism may mean sailing close to the wind sometimes, but the aim is to avoid capsizing. She explained the position to me.

'OK. We have only two methods that can be chased. The first is the biochemical search for PrP using what's called immunoblotting, and the second is the immunogold method of staining what are called scrapie associated fibrils in the brain tissue,' I said. 'Neither can give false positives.'

'If you can find the people to do the tests, we'll put up the money.'

Here's the funding – now find a lab

I telephoned everyone, but got negative replies for a whole range of reasons. Isabel Tang, however, had gone cheque-book in hand to the University of Nottingham. Annoyed with the way that the research into BSE had been carried out, and fed up with MAFF's attitude and the lack of money leaking out to good researchers in the universities, they had said yes.

Data on the cost of compensation paid to farmers for BSE became available in March 1995:

1988	£527,12
1989	£2,826,788
1990	£9,030,752
1991	£15,741,463
1992	£28,205,613
1993	£36,290,273
1994	£22,546,902

i.e. approximately £1000 per case, with the cost per case dropping in 1994 as the compensation rate dropped to the value of an older cow.

'Nottingham is going to need the samples and they will need to know exactly what to do as they have no experience,' she said.

'I could easily dig out the methods from the literature if that's what you want,' I told her. 'But it will simply not be good enough. They will need antibodies for the experiments, and I can't see MAFF happily handing them over unless they know what the tests are for.'

'Isn't there anywhere that will give us some? Surely someone must be interested in seeing if we're eating infected cattle?' Isabel was quite right, of course. The ones who were interested were of course the Germans!

Cases of BSE had been reported in the offspring of cattle exported from the UK to Portugal. When the media chased it up they found that there had been 12 by August 1995. One had actually come from Holland and they thought that none had been fed UK ruminant protein.   July 1995.

I wrote to Heino Diringer and asked if I could come to his department in Berlin to learn about immunoblotting. Diringer had been in the field for a long time and was quite convinced that the prion theory was misleading. He was working hard, had produced a number of recent publications and was known to help innocent researchers. After a lot of hard work I returned to the UK with a wad of helpful information. The one thing that was worrying, however, was that the test was clearly of low sensitivity: many cattle that were actually infected would turn out to be negative because it was too early in their incubation period for the test to pick them up. The other thing that the Germans gave me which turned out to be very useful was some antibody solution against the prion protein. Generally the better the antibody, the better the test, and it was feared that the antibodies supplied by MAFF to groups outside their own was poor. Isabel rushed the information and the vial of antiserum off to Nottingham University to get them going.

Smith et al reported that a third dairy farmer who had had a case of BSE on his farm had died of confirmed CJD. Later it was admitted that another was dying similarly. *Lancet*, 30 September 1995.

One of the most important pieces of information concerning the epidemiology of BSE became available in March 1995. There was a steady in-herd rate, i.e. the proportion of a herd that was infected that died annually of BSE.

Year	National rate (%)	Within-herd rate (%)
1988	0.08	1.78
1989	0.18	1.91
1990	0.35	2.16
1991	0.63	2.44
1992	0.92	2.72
1993	0.86	2.43
1994	0.59	2.05

When the figures are corrected for apparent under-reporting the in-herd rate remains at approximately 2.7% after 1992.

Harash Narang was happy to go ahead and test the brain samples from the cattle. The fragments were put on to the copper transmission electron microscope grids and stained for viewing at the University of Manchester Electron Microscopy (EM) Unit. He searched the grids and their fine films of tissue for the particles that represented infection, which he found in 8 of the 28 for which we had good samples. It was made quite clear to the manager of the unit what was happening and there seemed to be no problem. EM was used regularly on samples of CJD, which must be considered much more dangerous to humans, so there could be little relative risk from BSE. The problem arose when Isobel Tang visited and the manager was told who she was. The next day Harash was asked to pack up and go, but by this time the tests had been done.

'Don't you think that 8 out of 28 is rather high?' I enquired of Harash. 'I was only expecting to find around 6 or perhaps fewer.' Although I had predicted that between 1.1 million and 3.2 million cattle that we were eating might be infected, I still had not expected such a large figure. One of the other epidemiological statisticians had suggested that the figure would be even higher, between 30 and 40%.

'Well, that's what was there and I can't argue. The researcher was with me and saw what I found.' He was right. I had even asked a member of the Religious Studies Department in the University of Manchester to come over to the EM Unit just to confirm that Harash was actually carrying out the experiments that he said he was doing. If it ever came to court there had to be as many independent witnesses as possible. So when Harash found that the numbers were so high I had to believe him.

By this time Isabel was coming back with more information from Nottingham concerning the immunoblotting.

'They're going to take much longer than expected. But we must push ahead with the programme. The managers are determined that this one must get going, but it will only be going out in November.'

'What! You said it would be in August, then it was September. What's happened? I've been trying my best with John Kent to make sure that the article was ready to go out on exactly the same day as the programme.'

'That's how it is. We've tried our best, but that's the slot: 13 November at 8.30p.m. The most watched programme of the evening.' She saw my face drop. I had risked ruining my career, my social life and my love life to get this information out to the population. 'Don't worry,' she added, 'it's certain now. And anyway the immunoblotting is going well. We should have an answer from them in time. Whatever happens, MAFF won't have a chance to come back at us.'

By that time I had spoken to a number of the major researchers in the field. They had repeated Harash Narang's technique (though not with cattle) and found that it worked. All I could do was tell Isabel that the chance of MAFF admitting they had been hiding information would be extremely slim.

Preparing for the cameras

I was to go in front of the cameras myself in a laboratory at Manchester University. Isabel asked me some basic questions about BSE to calm me down, then she went at it in earnest.

Two groups announced that a 16-year-old and an 18-year-old had died of CJD. There had only been four teenagers with the disease reported in the world before this. *Lancet,* 28 October 1995.

'What proportion were infected in 1988? What proportion are infected that we are eating now? How many that we eat have actually shown signs of disease before being slaughtered?'

By this time I had answers prepared to all but a few of them. The complex mathematics needed to explain the under-reporting was deemed to be too tough to put across, and the simple answers that the TV people needed were not scientifically valid enough. I had been driving down the motorway asking myself the questions, waking up in the middle of the night answering them. When this programme came out I was going to be quite ready to prevent MAFF getting away with misleading answers.

Will Patterson rang up. He had spent a year putting data together to indicate the position on BSE to the public health professions. I could provide the scientific publications that my filing cabinets were bursting with in order to help him along, but he knew that a major risk was being taken and did not need me to point it out. He had sent his article to many of the major public health officials and experts in the country in advance of publication to ask their opinions. Minimal problems had arisen. Indeed, many of the recipients had urged him on. Many of the doctors concerned were now becoming aware that they had been kept in the dark about BSE risks and that the information coming from the Department of Health was probably true but inadequate. The paper was to be published in October and would create a minor stir.

Things were pushing forward too fast for me by October. The *British Food Journal*, which was about to publish the article by John Kent and myself showing the problems with MAFF BSE statistics, had sent it out to reviewers. This was essential, for when it came out it had to be completely watertight. One of the reviewers was determined that the information concerning human risk should be taken out. The other reviewer seemed equally determined that it should stay in, and this one eventually succeeded. A lot of the minor wording was altered to sound better, and the data from my interviews of farmers at the Yorkshire show had to be taken out because it was not adequately validated. Some of the statistics indicating how the under-reporting was calculated in a second way were removed.

Anyway, the paper was to go ahead as the longest piece the journal had ever published. I got back to the publishers, MCB in Bradford, and begged them to postpone publication until 13 November. They said that their responsibility was to their readership and the delaying of the distribution of a journal was unacceptable, but they would do what they could. Eventually they sent out copies of the article, to arrive on the 13th, to a list of people involved with BSE that I supplied. MCB would be using this as an opportunity to build up the number of international researchers who knew of their journal, but it was a fantastic opportunity for us.

Professor Heino Diringer, a major researcher into TSEs, explained his hypothesis in the *Lancet*: 'Proposed link between transmissible spongiform encephalopathies of man and animals.' He said that scrapie could indeed be transferred from one species to another and indeed would change its ability to infect in the new species. Somehow we had to explain why so many cases of sporadic cases of CJD (ones not associated with other members of the family being affected) had been seen and how these appeared to be due to infections. If we were not getting them directly from sheep, as would be indicated by the epidemiology, perhaps we were getting them from cattle after scrapie had been transferred to them. This would have serious consequences. *Lancet*, 4 November 1995.

Two helpers put hundreds of photocopies of the article into envelopes. Junior doctors at the hospital in Burnley had translated summaries of the article into French, German and Spanish, so whichever language seemed to be the right one a copy went too. In with them went the data concerning the information that I was going to put on to the Internet, and copies of Will Patterson's article if the recipient seemed to be someone who would appreciate it.

Back in the laboratory, the telephone rang. It was Brian Marchant from the Agricultural Commission at the EC, who had just received the article.

'Are you telling me that much of the data given to us by MAFF has been misleading?' he asked.

'I really don't know what they've been telling you. But what they've been telling the House of Commons has certainly been misleading. Truthful, but economical with it, would probably be a good description. What I'm not at all sure about is whether the people at the top are actually lying. I think they probably believe what they're telling you. There are no villains in this one. Just a lot of money and human lives,' I said.

'I haven't actually read it yet, but if it's what I think this is very serious stuff.'

'All I can do is ask you not to get your information concerning BSE from MAFF, and to try to find sources that have nothing to lose if beef sales drop,' I said. But I didn't think that would be easy, as almost everyone who advised on the subject was in some way associated with MAFF.

It was Monday, 13 November, the day when the *World in Action* programme was to be on the air. I then learned from another journalist that the BBC were putting out a programme immediately before mine, but this time showing that people were worried about BSE. It was going to be quite a night. Until 8p.m. I was talking to journalists and then everything was quiet.

Over the previous two days small amounts of information on the programme had trickled through to the press. The *World in Action* team had made sure that it was not full of incomprehensible statistics and heavy science, but it would still show that there was more to BSE than met the eye.

I went to watch the programme in the common room with a group of junior doctors. It began with a determined-looking, slightly thin man in a white coat, wearing round, heavy-framed glasses, sitting in a laboratory. It was me. 'People have no way of knowing if a beefburger they eat is infected or not,' he said. The point of no return. This was shown even before the music and titles. I could see that it was going to be a heavy thirty minutes.

233

Initially it explained that there had been an outbreak of mad cow disease in the UK and that there was a similar disease called CJD which we would be expecting to get if BSE infected humans. Steven Churchill, a 19-year-old, had died recently and his picture was shown. Peter Warhurst, a dairy farmer, had also died. The question was whether or not the rest of us were being put at risk.

The programme focused on an interview with the Chief Veterinary Officer, Sir Keith Meldrum, who had many times made statements concerning BSE that I had considered scientifically unacceptable in terms of human risk. He had been the CVO for many years and was used to handling the media, so I wasn't expecting any interesting outbursts. First they asked if he was happy with the way that BSE was being handled. He went through the way in which they were sure that no BSE-infected material reached the plate of the consumer. 'There is no evidence that there is any threat to humans from BSE. We have all these controls in place to protect the public.'

The programme explained that many cattle were dying every week – the current rate was 300 – that were found to have BSE. The question was whether others with the disease were not being reported. My God, Isabel hadn't said anything about this! I had given her the data showing that we were eating cattle with symptoms, but I didn't think she could actually demonstrate it.

'A dairy farmer wants a case of BSE on his farm like a hole in the head. Many of them would do anything to get rid of them – anything at all.' This was Geoff Moss, a farmer who had dealt with BSE cases for some time and was on a list of names and addresses that I had given her. MAFF had told me they were going to 'deal' with him in about 1992 when they found that some farmers were actually buying up cattle with BSE symptoms to claim the compensation from MAFF.

Then it was the turn of Richard North, a food safety

adviser from Bradford with whom I had dealt in the past. He explained that it was much easier for the farmer to ship a case of BSE to market than to take the risk of reporting it to the veterinary officer, who might not actually accept it as BSE. If that happened, of course, the farmer would lose a lot of money because it would show more symptoms and probably could not be sold for human food.

The film showed the markets at which Geoff Moss picked out three cattle that might have BSE. Moss had picked out 2000 of them over the years yet no cattle with symptoms of BSE should be put to market; but they are. He described how an animal appeared early in the disease: 'Funny on its legs, holding its ears back, flicking them more than usual, continually licking its nose.' All this had been filmed with a secret camera. The market vet had picked out no cattle at all that might have BSE. A few weeks later a second hidden camera had been used to show the MAFF veterinary officer looking at the cattle that Moss had picked from the market. 'Typical, classic,' he said, describing how these cases just had to be BSE.

The programme jumped back to Meldrum. He said he was absolutely confident that his inspectors would pick out all cattle with symptoms of BSE at the markets and went on: 'All cattle have an ante-mortem inspection when the cow is at rest,' indicating that if the cases were not picked out at the market they would be found at the abattoir. Again the *World in Action* programme-makers had gone to an independent source of information.

David Statham, an environmental health officer, made it clear that the methods used for inspection were not likely to find a case of BSE. The programme simply quoted the statistics again, showing that so few cases had been found at an abattoir in a whole year (whereas three were found by Moss in just two markets) that this inspection could not work.

Richard North was back then, explaining that a placid

cow might well be a bit more irritable if it had BSE but the chance of picking it out at the abattoir was nil. This was hot stuff.

Graham Medley, an epidemiologist at Warwick University, stated that the Ministry had always been unwilling to release data which would enable anyone to calculate the number of BSE cases being eaten. He had tried repeatedly to find out what was going on but the data was always refused.

Meldrum again. 'We hold nothing back. Totally open policy. All the data that we have is made known.' He was asked again and again by Isabel Tang whether the number of infected cattle we were eating was known. Meldrum refused to answer, saying that they thought of it in a different way and that they slaughtered all the cattle with symptoms. He was asked at least three times and each time dodged the question, getting hotter under the collar every time. He was absolutely determined not to say that we were eating infected cattle and that they knew how many. Eventually Isabel asked him a similar question about the number of infected cattle we were eating. 'I've answered that one already,' he said.

'I'm sorry, Mr Meldrum, but you haven't,' she replied. He got up rapidly and marched towards the camera, telling them to turn it off.

'His credibility must be in tatters,' said one of the doctors in the room with me.

'Well,' Isabel said, 'it would be possible to find out the number of infected cattle that we were eating if only we tested some of the cattle passing through the abattoir.' Apparently MAFF had repeatedly refused to carry out such tests.

Richard North made things clear. 'The reason why they don't take random tests is that they would be appalled at what they would find. They would find a much higher number than current figures show.'

Meldrum came back: 'We have looked at that and taken a very careful view.' He went on to say that the results would be meaningless and so they did not carry out the tests. Yet he must have known that I and various other people had written repeatedly asking for random testing.

They then went over to Harash Narang in the Electron Microscopy Unit in Leeds. They admitted that his method was controversial but then showed that of 31 cases of dairy cattle slaughtered for human food which he had tested, 8 had been found positive for the tubulofilamentous particles which Harash said 'only exist in BSE cases'. He also made it clear that this could be an underestimate.

Isabel had obviously given Medley the data that I used with Kent and asked him to check our findings. Pictures of his computer screen went with statements that approximately 40,000 infected cattle were being slaughtered and eaten. For every diagnosed cow two were being eaten. I let out a long breath. I had been begging that he would find the same as I did, and he roughly did.

Clothing and equipment: before removal, all items of reusable waterproof clothing should be washed in detergent and rinsed well. Items may then be removed and immersed in sodium hypochlorite solution containing 20,000 parts per million available chlorine for one hour and then rinsed. All disposable clothing and equipment should be double bagged to await removal to the incinerator. Non-disposable equipment should either be immersed in sodium hypochlorite as above or autoclaved.

This is an extract from the Advisory Committee on Dangerous Pathogens' document 'Precautions for Work with Human and Animal Transmissible Spongiform Encephalopathies'. It was aimed at people working in labs, but the same directions were not prescribed for those working in butchers' shops, canteens or supermarkets, let alone preparing meals at home. It is difficult to imagine

---

someone taking a piece of liver out of a supermarket tray in order to cook it but having to put plastic gloves on first and incinerating them afterwards.

The document itself is excellent, but what it does show is that it is both impractical and uneconomic to take the necessary steps to avoid risk in the home or at work.

Meldrum had sat down again by this time and accepted that two cattle incubating BSE would be eaten for every one with symptoms. That was why they had a control programme. In animals taken to slaughter, he asserted, the infectivity was removed – if present at all – because the tissues with infectivity were removed.

Immediately the film showed how a piece of liver from an infected animal would be treated in the laboratory, and compared it to the way it got treated in the home.

And so it went on. That programme was going to be the sinking of MAFF's 'Don't worry about it' position on BSE and the start of open discussion on the subject. People would no longer believe what government officers told them about BSE and would want independent scientists to release data. Isabel was the heroine of the hour and, although for the time being the farmers and butchers would be after her, they would be saved by her in the end. But that was yet to come. Lacey, of course, was delighted.

A media explosion

Next day the phone did not stop ringing. Every newspaper from the *Sun* to the *Independent* was on my trail and wanted to know the full story. The original aim was to give them the number of the Internet and tell them to look up the data, but they often claimed that they had no access to it or that they must know straightaway.

On 25 November 1995 the *British Medical Journal* published a series of six articles concerning the risk of BSE to humans.

Jeffrey Almond from Reading University put forward information showing that we simply do not know enough about the disease to pretend any certainty in this matter. He demanded that research should go ahead into all possible aspects in order to be sure.

Paul Brown from the National Institute of Health in Washington, known to be convinced that BSE was not a risk to humans, said that the jury was still out. In other words we would have to wait and see what happened to the number of cases of CJD before we claimed that BSE was not a risk.

Ros Ridley and Harry Baker from Cambridge said that the risk was low but we did not know yet.

Geoff Roberts, now from Smith Kline Beecham, asked if BSE could infect humans at all, and if it could, when would we find out? His answers were that the science was so difficult that we might have to carry out massive research to answer them. This was not a risk that you took and then waited to see if you died.

Kenneth Tyler, Professor of Neurology in Denver, Colorado, attempted to look at the relative risks of different amounts of disease to which people would be exposed and how some groups might be more at risk than others. 'Since no effective treatment of prion disease currently exists, the emphasis of public health measures must be on preventing disease.' Again he demanded research.

Sheila Gore put over the most important data: 'More than happenstance: CJD disease in farmers and young adults.' She showed that the chance of the farmers' cases appearing as they had was 10,000 to 1. This should not be considered as just a freak occurrence and should be investigated.

A new hero emerged: Sir Bernard Tomlinson, the retired neuropathologist from Gateshead, who made some specific and direct statements on *You and Yours*, which went out on Radio 4 around lunchtime.

The interviewer, James Erlichman, used to work for the *Guardian* and I had often sent him information there. James came to Burnley to ask me for my part of the story.

'Stephen, Sir Bernard actually said it.'

'Said what?' This was before the radio programme went out.

'He made it quite clear that he wouldn't eat specific foods. He stated that certain bovine offals should be considered as dangerous. It's in the can. They're going to put it on the radio!'

My jaw dropped. For a long time it had been myself, Helen Grant, Lacey and a few other campaigners who had been demanding things like bovine liver to be taken out of the human diet, and we were just put down as dissidents. Here was one of the major advisers to the Department of Health stating that the risk was unacceptable.

A couple of days later he rang me from London. 'Hey, Steve, it's going to be half an hour of programme this time. The whole *You and Yours* is going to be about BSE. It's going to hit the ceiling. We've issued a press release this morning, and it's been on all the BBC news programmes already. This is going to be the big one.'

He was right. Tomlinson did not sit on any fences. For my part I made it clear that risks were being taken and that we were eating infected cattle. Narang was open about the research that was not being done because it was being prevented, and about how he had been blighted because he was good. Helen Grant made it clear that this was unacceptable.

The newspapers exploded again: this was front page news. James Erlichman went in to work the following day to find cuttings from every newspaper stuck on a board. This was first-class journalism and the *You and Yours* editor knew it. On James's desk was a bottle of champagne.

The Sunday Times did a survey of researchers in the field. Professor Almond was convinced there might be a link between BSE and CJD and demanded substantial research. Colin Blakemore, the Professor of Physiology at Oxford, made it clear that the risks taken were quite unacceptable and that he had stopped his children eating any beef since the beginning of the epidemic. Gareth Roberts, the major neuroanatomist with Smith Kline Beecham, stated that he was eating fewer beef products than before but for various reasons and not just because of BSE. Thomas Stuttaford, the *Times* doctor, was adamant that he did not eat specific bovine tissues because of BSE. However, certain people were not so punchy. Sir Richard Doll, the epidemiologist from Oxford, made it clear that he thought the risk was too small to worry about, and John Pattison, the new man in charge of SEAC, stated that there was no current evidence that BSE gave rise to CJD and he had not changed his eating habits. It was, nevertheless, quite clear that people were coming out of the woodwork and speaking up.

On 1 December *The Times* devoted two articles and an editorial to the subject.

The drumbeat over BSE was insistent. Warnings were appearing over meat pies, pâtés, liver and so on. Major internationally respected researchers were declaring BSE a danger. The Government's position gave no comfort, as the tightening of regulations just meant that we must have been taking risks already. Just because we had not seen a large increase in CJD cases did not mean that we would not in ten years' time. There was not enough data to justify taking a view that there was no risk. 'If, in ten years' time, people start dying of an appalling degenerative disease contracted as a result of eating British beef products, the legal and moral liability of the Government will be too ghastly to contemplate.'

It demanded that the regulations already in place were enforced, which did not seem to be the case at that time. It stated that the market would make decisions for the Government, and the beef industry would be in a serious position. The value of cattle from uninfected herds would rise and the rest would drop. Imports would rise.

'The Government for its part must look at the growing tendency of courts, especially the European Court of Justice, to award very high levels of damages. The punitive element of such awards is likely to be particularly high in cases where a government is showing reckless disregard to the health of its citizens.'

The media stories continued at full pace. A woman died of CJD in Manchester Royal Infirmary. She had been pregnant and the baby had been born by Caesarian section ten weeks early. The *Sun* gave this a lot of space. I had written to the consultant suggesting that the baby be tested for CJD, because when this had happened before in Japan the baby's blood was infective. There was no reply, but the doctor must have been over-run with media attention and he had probably been in contact with the CJD Unit in Edinburgh.

On 7 December Hugh Bayley, MP for York, went straight to the point during Prime Minister's Question Time. 'As a parent of school-age children I speak on behalf of many parents when I tell the Prime Minister that the Government have failed to convince the public or school caterers that British beef is safe. Will the Prime Minister, as a matter of urgency, make sure that the Department of Health issues genuinely independent advice about this matter to reassure parents?'

Mr Major tried his best. 'Of course this is an important matter for schools and for the safety of consumers as a whole. I have sought and received advice that there is currently no scientific evidence that BSE can be transmitted to humans or that eating beef causes CJD. That is not in question. I am also advised that beef is a safe and wholesome product. The Chief Medical Officer's advice is clear – there is no evidence that eating beef causes CJD in humans.'

> MAFF announced on 13 December 1995 that all that was needed to stop humans being at risk was to prevent mechanically recovered meat being taken from the spinal column. They said that there was no shortage of research funding. They said that there was no risk to humans. They said that work was being done.

This fell on stony ground, however, and Bayley called on the Government to set up an independent inquiry under Professor Sir Bernard Tomlinson. By this time numerous groups were calling on Government action and little notice was taken of Mr Major's position on the subject.

BSE had been all over the UK media for four weeks, and in the German and Japanese press too. Already schools were removing beef from their meals. A directive came from a London group to schools across the UK, stating that there was a current risk of unknown size associated with BSE and while this risk was present it would be difficult to justify feeding children beef products at school. Several counties, including Lancashire, Kent, Staffordshire, Humberside and Oxfordshire, took beef off school menus.

Many other schools did so independently, particularly in Glamorgan and Yorkshire. Oldham, the place from which the lady in Manchester came who had recently died of CJD in pregnancy, was the first to take beef off the list.

CHAPTER TWELVE

The answer nobody wanted to find

I went in to work on Tuesday, 19 March 1996 and sat down to deal with the business of the day. By 11a.m. the laboratory had produced most of the reports that needed to go to the wards and I was sifting through them to look for infections that were going to be important. The telephone rang. It was James Erlichman.

'Headless chickens, Steve,' he said. 'Apparently there are alarm bells ringing all over the Department of Health. They say there's going to be some enormous announcement about BSE.'

'Have we any idea what they're actually going to say? I mean, they could be simply presenting the Commons with data showing that we've been eating huge numbers of infected cattle. We knew that several years ago,' I replied.

'It was no minor contact who gave me the news. It's not just a back-down. This is going to be government-shaking news.'

I said I would ring various contacts around the country and try to dig out what was going to happen. If this was the admission that people had been exposed to unacceptable levels of disease, I ought to be ready. Nobody seemed to know what it was about, but none of the SEAC contacts was available. Very private news, then: either it never existed or it was going to be political dynamite.

At midnight the telephone rang next to my bed. It was *GMTV*, the early morning news broadcast that did its best to put over interviews at breakfast-time.

'Good morning, Dr Dealler,' the caller said, 'you won't have seen today's *Daily Mirror*, I suppose, but I should tell you that it claims that the DoH are going to admit in the Commons today that BSE infects humans. Do you think we could interview you tomorrow morning?' This was going to be at 7a.m. and 8a.m., the peak slots.

If there was a day in which we could somehow get over to the public that BSE was not the riskless irrelevance that we were being told it was this was going to be it.

By the time I got to the cameras, which they had set up in a lab, *GMTV* had already had a denial from the DoH that there was going to be any announcement on the subject. Mr Gardiner, the BSE expert from the National Farmers' Union, was saying that this could be a media hype and that viewers should not take any notice until the Government made their pronouncement. I sat in the same seat as I had done for *GMTV* in the past and told them the data about risks from BSE: how we had already put the population at risk with BSE and how, in public health terms, this risk was unacceptably high.

From 9a.m. my telephone was jammed with calls. I tried to get back to everyone and made a list of things that Stephen Dorrell, the new Minister of Health, was possibly going to say so that I could fax it to all of them. By about 11a.m. the DoH had withdrawn its denial of a speech by the Minister. The press knew that this was going to be one of the most important speeches ever.

> In January 1996 the Spongiform Encephalopathy Research Campaign sent SEAC a five-page list of specific research into aspects that did not currently seem to be adequately covered.

By three o'clock the telephone had stopped ringing. Everyone was watching the television coverage of Parliament and the press conference at which SEAC experts were announcing the fears. One of the radio broadcasters told me, almost word by word, what was being said as it came over.

> In 1996 it became clear from MAFF's own data that 48% of abattoirs did not handle meat products fully to MAFF regulations.

Ten cases of CJD had appeared in younger people (under 42 years of age). The most important aspect of them was that they were similar to each other both in clinical symptoms and in the pathological damage that appeared in the brain and could be seen under the microscope. Normally CJD is quite variable and the disease affects many parts of the brain, but with these cases the damage had been done in similar areas to those found in cows with BSE.

'We are seriously concerned about what is going to happen next. That is why we have asked for intense surveillance so we can measure the scale of the problem over the coming months and years.' Professor Pattison admitted that the coming numbers of cases of BSE in humans, calculated on current information, could represent a major public health problem.

'There may be quite a few more cases. It is totally unpredictable, and at one extreme there is a risk of an epidemic,' said Dr Will. 'I believe this is a new phenomenon. There is reason for major concern.'

Apparently the cases had started to appear in 1994, when there were six, and continued in large numbers in 1995; a further four have so far been diagnosed. It now seems that there are two patients in the same clinical group who have not yet died and for whom there is no reliable diagnosis by microscopic histology. It was assumed that the people had become infected well before the specified offals ban of November 1989 and that, because of that ban, the ongoing risk to humans was minimal.

Dr Kenneth Calman, the Government's Chief Medical Officer, said he would continue to eat beef as part of a varied and balanced diet. Stephen Dorrell insisted that children were no more at risk than adults and admitted that the Government had considered slaughtering 11 million cattle – the entire national herd – to decrease any potential risk to humans. Douglas Hogg announced that tougher regulations for the slaughter and handling of bovine carcasses would be brought in so that beef could be eaten with confidence. He did not believe the findings would damage consumer confidence. He said that cattle over 30 months must be deboned in specific licensed plants supervised by the Meat Hygiene Service. There would be a complete prohibition of the use of meat and bone meal in animal feed.

'New infection leads to mad cow disease.' *The Times*, Thursday, 21 March 1996.

'Beef warning starts panic.' *Guardian*, Thursday, 21 March 1996.

'Scientists fear ban must now spread to lamb.' *Sunday Times*, 24 March 1996.

'Cabinet plot to stop beef alert.' *Observer*, Sunday, 24 March 1996.

'Beef age pledge by EU.' *Guardian*, Saturday, 30 March 1996.

'Tories want to scrap food safety rules.' *Independent on Sunday*, 31 March 1996.

Uproar is the only word to describe the response from the press. They had been repeatedly misled by MAFF. They had been given data, over and over again, showing that the disease was disappearing and that, as there had been no increase in CJD, we were completely past the problem. When the journalists talked about Hogg's claim that consumer confidence in beef would remain buoyant, they did so with complete disdain.

I could not believe how they could get away with this volte-face after Calman had had his name on major newspaper advertisements in November announcing that beef was safe, after Rob Will had given a lecture two weeks earlier in the House of Commons telling 40 political and food trade visitors that we should assume BSE not to be infective to humans, after Richard Kimberlin had spent many years as adviser to the drug companies and food trades telling them that BSE was not a risk and would go away. Their loss of personal credibility must have been depressing to them, but it was impressive that they had the nerve to stand up and say that they had been wrong. It was particularly impressive that Dorrell had been willing to make the statement, even though he must have realised its implications.

The following morning Professor Lacey, who had been claiming the potential risk of BSE for six years, was a presence in most of the newspapers. He regarded it as one of the most disgraceful episodes in this country's history, he said, and demanded a full and independent inquiry into the conduct of the Government and the way it had used and misused scientific advisers. He made it plain that the repeated claims by the Government that advisers were the source of all policy on the subject were quite unacceptable. We in the field had all known that the small range of people in SEAC included only a small group who understood the subject fully, and even these were known to regard BSE as a minor risk. One of the members was a vet interested in the subject, another an expert in foot and mouth disease, another a histologist, another a retired manager of a veterinary research laboratory. Even the chairman had been an expert on the common cold. Yet the Government was making it clear to the press that these were the national experts on the subject of BSE and that they were taking their advice from them. 'Who are these experts?' said Lacey on television. 'I've never heard of them as experts.' The press and independent researchers had known it as the Kimberlin Committee before Pattison had arrived. He replaced Tyrrell as chairman in late 1995, and a number of experts in public health, virology, prion disease and epidemiology, as well as Ray Bradley, had joined at the beginning of 1996.

'Why on earth didn't they warn the Government of the potential risks in 1991?' I asked a journalist. 'I had the data ready in 1993, but they had quite enough information back in 1991 to be able to predict the broad level of risk that had already been taken and was being taken currently.'

'It's always better to be wrong but politically correct than right but politically wrong,' he said, sounding like a Confucius-he-say statement. 'Everyone will have been aching to hear good news. People on committees get very practised at playing the game. Patronage dies quickly in committees that don't provide the politicians with what they want to hear.'

'But thank God for John Pattison,' I replied, 'the man who had the nerve to make the statement that human risk is not necessarily low.'

Beef exports are banned

On Thursday the 21st journalists started hounding me immediately I arrived in the lab. They now knew that the 'expert' committee had on some advice been consistently wrong for six years in its advice to the Government. They realised that the ever-tightening restrictions on the meat trade over this period must always have been an admission that the previous restrictions had been inadequate. They understood that the public simply weren't going to believe what the DoH and MAFF were telling them in terms of beef safety. By this time the beef markets were empty, supermarket sales had virtually stopped, and schools around the country had banned the use of beef products. The journalists had contacts with the schools that had been ordered by the Government to bring back beef to the children's diet in 1994 after it had been felt by the teachers to be a potential risk.

Television and radio stations from all around the world were homing in on the subject, and bans on British beef were imposed by France and Belgium. Immediately Douglas Hogg declared that this would be taken to the European Union as an unlawful action and these countries would be ordered to resume imports.

'How on earth could he think the EU will order this?' asked someone from a major newspaper. 'There's no chance they'll comply.'

By the end of the week the European Veterinary Committee had declared that British beef should be banned not just from Europe but worldwide. The UK Government immediately stated that it was not up to that committee to make such a judgement. By the following Tuesday, however, the EU had made it a fully lawful decision, as announced by Franz Fischler, head of the Agriculture Committee.

Vicky Rimmer was admitted to be a case of CJD in 1996. She was in a coma and dying at the age of 18.

Peter Hall died of CJD at 20. He died slowly over several years.

Anne Richardson died of CJD at 41.

None of these people had any genetic reasons to go down with the disease.   March 1996.

On the Thursday afternoon I had promised to give a lecture to the virology group at the Public Health Laboratory in Preston on the methods of diagnosis of spongiform encephalopathies. They were an excellent group and clearly knew that this was the subject of the day.

'Look, there's going to be immense amounts of money available,' I told them. 'This is going to be one of the biggest research directions in the UK. You must get into it and don't let the Public Health Laboratory Service tell you otherwise.'

Anne Pearson, 29 years old, was admitted to have died of CJD at Kent and Canterbury Hospital. This has not yet reached the statistics of the number of cases of BSE in humans. March 1996.

Three weeks previously I had arranged with Grampian TV to appear on *We the Jury* on 22 March as the man claiming that we should worry about BSE. The opposing viewpoint was to be put by a man from the NFU in Scotland (where there had been much less BSE). I was flown up to Aberdeen and met Will Patterson on the way. He was the only expert on the public health of BSE and had been quoted by the *York Evening Express* about a year earlier as claiming it to be a risk of which no calculation could be certain at present. His employers had demanded that he withdraw and deny all statements that the newspaper had printed. He must have been furious: it was a dreadful insult to someone who knew the subject. It turned out that Grampian had asked him to speak as well and we discussed the horrors of the previous few days.

The aim was to convince the jury, 12 good local people, that beef was either safe or it wasn't. They were asked beforehand what they thought, and it was clear that BSE was not really a worry. The major speakers got two minutes each but then the groups behind us moved in. Helen Grant made it plain that what we thought was just beef certainly was not. We should realise that infectivity would be everywhere, if only because of the way in which the meat was produced. Will Pattison brought out the information from the Advisory Committee on Dangerous Pathogens showing that BSE should be assumed to be in many other tissues than the ones that were banned, and the parents of a recent CJD case told the tear-jerking story of the slow death of their son.

The most frightening person was someone from the other side, a Dr Watson who had been on the Southwood Committee (the one that informed MAFF that BSE was not a risk to humans and that we could continue eating the brain of cattle). He claimed that there had not been enough data with which to take aggressive action in 1989. This was clearly incorrect. There was quite enough data even then that BSE could not be assumed to be non-infective to humans, and quite enough data to show the potential risk that it would present.

The jury came down eight to four in favour of the idea that beef was unsafe, although the phone-in group was eight to four the other way. I knew that the market for Aberdeen Angus was going to crash in the following few days, and it is difficult to be the messenger carrying the bad news (partly because such messengers often end up being shot).

A physiotherapist from north of Manchester indicated that another farmer, a man in his late forties, had been reported as dying of CJD. The death had taken place about a year earlier and was not to be confused with the case of the farmer near Bury who had died. The physiotherapist had been told not to tell anyone.   March 1996.

Immediately afterwards I was shuffled away to a studio for Canadian TV and begged to be on the farming programme the following morning. By the time I got to the party that Grampian was holding afterwards, all the experts who claimed the safety of beef had left, and I talked to the members of the jury. They had been staggered by the data that I had put forward: the sheer number of infected cattle we were eating, the potential calculated risk. One of them was a plump and entertaining butcher who had seen a case of neurological disease in a cow 30 years earlier in the Orkney Islands. The cow had been shot and buried whole, but he could remember where and said he could dig it up again.

Alarm bells were ringing in the meat markets by Saturday the 23rd. Bans were being imposed by countries around the world, and the internal market was drying up too. McDonald's had announced that they would not be selling beefburgers made from UK beef; all the major fast food groups followed suit. Sainsbury's had slashed the prices of their meat but it was still on the shelves.

Demands for tough action

The SEAC committee had been told by MAFF and the DoH to decide what advice should be given on stopping beef being eaten by children and on the slaughter of further cattle. I would have hated to be in their position. To be asked to make decisions on a condition that would possibly cause hundreds of deaths and to do it without adequate information was going to be a tough thing. I decided to send Pattison information on what I knew was going to take place over the following week. Unless I stopped it, the information showing a risk to children would reach the press. The possible risks from blood transfusions were going to get into the scientific press. The sheer lack of earlier research into the major aspects of BSE was going to be seen as quite unacceptable by Parliament. I told him that the slaughter of cattle was going to be demanded, if not by the press, then by the population or the NFU. Somehow, there would be no confidence in UK beef unless major action was taken. SEAC and the Government must have realised, however, that if they said that children should not eat beef this was an admission that a risk had been taken with the lives of adults for the previous six years, and that they had permitted it. The letter was faxed off to various groups.

The following morning the NFU were already asking for the slaughter to go ahead but MAFF, which had already failed to get the EU to accept the safety of British beef, was not willing to agree. The sheer cost of such action, and the logistical problems involved in the incineration of 700,000 cattle a year, made it almost impossible for MAFF to go ahead without full Government support. Hopefully the EU would promise large amounts of funding through the Common Agricultural Policy.

I went down on Wednesday the 27th to speak to several MPs. They were unhappy about the information they were being given through SEAC and were looking for ways out of the problem. The possibility that errors might have been made by the Thatcher and Major Governments, but that subsequent administrations would end up paying the immense cost of a potential epidemic of CJD, was hard to take. All the way through I made it clear that research was the only way out of this one. We had to find methods of diagnosis, we had to find methods of treatment for the disease, and we had to find out how many people were actually incubating the disease at present.

After the meeting I went upstairs to the room where the Agriculture Committee was interviewing advisers on BSE. Sitting on the panel and answering questions were Dr Calman, Rob Will and Richard Kimberlin, who had given advice that BSE was not a risk despite all the information that I had given them over the previous years. Even Keith Meldrum, the Chief Veterinary Officer, was present. This was the man who had refused to tell people the number of infected cattle they were eating or my calculated risks that this entailed. Pattison was there too.

As the meeting ended I walked over to the group answering the questions and handed a letter to Kenneth Calman, who turned around, smiled and took my hand. I told him that I demanded to be heard and was very annoyed. Afterwards I felt dreadful about what I had said to him – there had been no need for it.

'Don't worry,' said my sister with whom I was staying. 'You aren't a politically desirable person anyway, and politeness is often accepted in retrospect.'

'I'll write to him and apologise. It's just that I've spoken to the members of his department so often and apparently been ignored, that seven years of frustration and six days of inadequate sleep took their toll.'

By Friday the 29th, the meeting at Turin of all the major leaders of the EU had taken place and a major promise of financial aid had been proposed by the members. Douglas Hogg had allegedly offered his resignation to the Prime Minister and it had been turned down. It had been an extraordinary and exhausting ten days.

The fear that is spreading in Europe

The German population were shown the information concerning BSE. A fatal disease, part of a group that was spread from one animal to another by eating infective tissue. They decided that UK beef was simply not worth the risk. While it was unknown whether the beef was infective or not, the claims by MAFF that we should therefore decide that it was safe was considered ridiculous by the German public. There was no need to eat UK beef, so why put one's children at risk? In 1990 the German Government decided that the risk was unacceptable and demanded that cattle from the UK not be imported.

This is quite a reasonable position to take but the British Goverment demanded that, as there was no proof of human risk, the EC must force the Germans to permit the importation to restart in the summer of 1990. A compromise was reached in that the British would only export cattle from herds known to be clear of disease and would only export meat off the bone (a difficult task). However, this proved difficult to enforce. By 1994 it had become clear that some farmers were not being asked at markets if their cattle were from an infected herd and so export was taking place using documents signed by vets saying that the cattle were from a BSE-free herd, when the vet had no way of knowing. The computer that was supposed to be involved in enforcement was doing nothing more than simply keeping statistics as it was admitted that information could not be given out concerning specific cattle as this would be in breach of the data-protection act.

Eventually the Europeans simply would not accept this and the admission in the House of Commons by Steven Dorrell that there may be an association between CJD and BSE was simply unacceptable to them. The UK had been repeatedly informing its EC partners that there was no risk and had hence been leading them up the garden path. Some of the British Government's advisers were those who advised the WHO and EC and it was therefore not surprising that the EC had taken the UK position as they had done earlier.

Initially the information reached the British press and by the next day the beef market in the UK was shattered. The population was now being told that the advice given earlier by MAFF and the DoH was incorrect but they should continue to eat beef anyway. It was impossible for them to accept this and the media showered them with much of the data that simply had not reached them over the last few years; showing that MAFF actually had plenty of data to warn of the risk that had been taken.

Within two days beef sales in every other country in the EC had crashed. So much beef had been exported from the UK that nobody knew if what they were buying was acceptable and safe. Initially it was Holland, France and Italy that banned British beef. Then it was the other countries; by the end of the following week over 20 countries had banned all British beef products. Germany however, now shown to have been 'right all the time', did not. Three of its provinces had, over the past year, banned British beef and the UK had threatened them with EC action to force the ban to be removed. There was no need for any legal action by this time as the Veterinary Committee at the EC decided that British beef products should not be exported to anywhere, never mind the EC countries. This was endorsed by the full EC a few days later despite Mr Hogg's protestations that British beef was completely without risk.

At the time of writing the beef market in the EC is still low and older UK cattle are being rounded up for slaughter. The Agriculture Commission has put forward large funds from the Common Agriculture budget to buy up 50,000 tons of beef from the European markets and restore the sales. British beef is now unwanted in the EC and signs are put up in European butchers' shops stating that none is on their counter.

CHAPTER THIRTEEN

What price ethics?

The silence after the storm

'So Lacey was right again?' asked the reporter.

'It certainly looks like it,' I replied. 'It seems that *all* the cattle in an affected herd in 1988 should be considered infected, and that a percentage of their offspring would go on to develop the disease if an environmental factor was present. He was right when he accused cook-chill food of being potentially risky, right when he suspected it of carrying listeria, and right when he expected microwave ovens to be unable to kill the bugs. Do you realise he's worried that BSE will never completely go away? Do you realise he's one of the group that has put the likelihood of humans developing CJD as a result of eating BSE as "unacceptably high"? Do you realise he's made it clear to MAFF numerous times that research into potential treatments must go ahead immediately? All I am is the research scientist who basically says "Yes, sir" and finds that what his boss has suggested was true. I was one of the pair who found listeria in the cook-chill food and in the food from which a woman caught the disease. I was the one who found out why microwave ovens don't kill bacteria in food reliably. Am I just fulfilling my leader's wishes? This time he had predicted vertical transmissions of BSE. Once again I had argued with him to begin with and then found out from MAFF's own data that he was right.'

'Are you actually certain of that though?' James Erlichman continued. 'If it's true it's pretty dreadful. It means that MAFF have actually been misleading everyone.'

'The problem with statistical analysis is that you *might* be wrong – but you can actually calculate the likelihood of that. Here all I can say is that MAFF's model of the disease simply does not fit their own data. They looked on it as something that's in the feed in little nuggets of infectivity. If your cow eats a big enough nugget it dies of BSE, and if it doesn't it's OK. What I've found is that a different model fits a lot better – but this happens to be Lacey's prediction that MAFF have already poured cold water on.'

'A lot better? How much better? Could they still be right?'

'The data virtually rules their plan out. All you have to do is stand back and look, which is what Lacey did. How can a random nugget in a random bag give rise to the picture that we have? Why should a herd that had had one infected animal be virtually certain to continue having the disease when there's about a 15% chance annually of a new herd becoming infected? It could be due to the supplier remaining infected, but the data doesn't even fit that. It is as if, up to 1988, herds have become infected and never uninfected. How can the in-herd rate of disease remain stable while the national rate rockets? How can the age distribution of cattle fit well into a solid stable curve from year to year when levels of infectivity in feed will have jumped and the disease supposedly transferred from one species to another? And, surely, when the feed containing infective material is stopped the disease should surely crash? But it hasn't.'

'I'll ask you again. You're accusing them of misleading everyone. Could they not have been aware of all this?'

'I think they could well not have been aware of it until 1993 – but then the roof caved in. It's quite likely they couldn't have carried out the statistical work that was done by Professor Kent. He's a very smart man indeed, and I would have been surprised if they could have reached the same level. Then again, they also denied being able to calculate the number of infected animals we were eating – and that's really quite simple. It's not quite a back-of-an-envelope job, but it can't be far from it. No, I'm told by people in the know that they were very afraid of vertical transmission by 1993, and they must have started doing their own maths on the subject by 1994. But they might not have been good enough to realise what was going on. That's if I'm right, of course, and there's a chance that I might not be! So they may well not have been misleading everyone – they may actually have thought they were right. Come on, James, if you were part of a terrific industry that was built up again after being ruined during the war to make the UK into a net producer of beef, would you like to face the implication that it might have been destroyed by MAFF's own recommendations to the rendering industry ten years earlier?'

'Are you aware that you're saying that the UK Government acted too slowly in banning the MBM in bovine food? You do realise you're saying it simply didn't act adequately to prevent the risk to humans *and should have known that*?'

'Certainly the data shows that MAFF was too late in banning ruminant remnant in the feed. By the time it got the rule in place it had completely missed the boat. As we can now see, 85% plus of the dairy cattle in the UK were infected by then. I don't think they could have done much better, though – and it's all very well looking from hindsight. As for the human risk, they were determined to take some of the most optimistic viewpoints and without adequate justification. Let's just hope they are right.'

'That's a bit grim, isn't it? When are we going to find out?' asked Erlichman.

'Well, it's too late to stop eating beef to improve your chances, so the experiment has been started and we may well have to wait until after the year 2000 to find out if humans are going to develop CJD as a result.'

'So you're the hero?'

'It would be nice to think that there were going to be any heroes in this at all. I didn't manage to stop people eating beef products from infected cattle. The whole thing is just sad. I tried my best, with Lacey, to indicate to the Government that they were taking an ethically unacceptable step in allowing UK beef to be eaten in the way it was. He went through the media and I tried all the official channels I could. I got nowhere. If there are any bad guys they are in the ranks of officialdom that played the government game and didn't think beyond it, and in Whitehall where data was massaged to show to the EC and the Minister. If there are any heroes they are the farmers who told the truth about their cows and the vets who told me what was going on.'

'Has anything good come out of this at all?'

'Oh yes, there have been amazing amounts of data concerning the epidemiology of TSEs. Some data is bound to be applied back to species that have died of other TSEs. Take the kudu – I'm now quite satisfied that it's likely to be passing its disease vertically. Also the environmental factor that's involved in allowing or causing the disease to be passed to offspring. We still have no idea what it might be, but it would explain very conveniently the fact that flocks of sheep exported to Australia and New Zealand only showed signs of scrapie in the animals actually exported and never in any of their offspring. It sounds as if there is a factor in the UK that keeps scrapie endemic, and if we start to look we may well be able to get rid of both that and BSE as well. After all, if the disease can't get to the next generation that's the end of it.'

'Hopeful!'

'Yes, hopeful, but I think I must be like that all the time. I'm one of those individuals who believe people are good unless proved bad – the sort the media must get fed up with because we don't make good headlines,' I said.

'Anything else good about BSE?' he continued the point.

'It might force us to look for treatments – and I do mean *force* us. An enormous experiment (with no ethical OK) has been taken with the human population. It's simply no good just waiting to see if humans start to die, because by that time – and that may well be after the year 2000 – it will be too late to do anything. Experiments in TSEs take a long time, and it's dreadful to think about looking for a potential treatment in five years' time when many people may already be well into their incubation period. Developing a drug takes a decade. We have to start looking now and pouring money into research as fast as we can. We have to look for methods of diagnosis that can be used long before symptoms appear and which can be done quickly. We must have methods to stop the disease being passed to *our* offspring.'

'Do you think that will happen?'

'No. None the less it would be ridiculous to assume that it won't. Maybe there will be no epidemic of CJD in humans at all, but I think there's some indication that the drugs developed to deal with it may well work on Alzheimer's disease as well. We must get on with this! I've tried to organise research into methods of treatment and diagnosis in the two major extra-MAFF labs, where I'm not necessarily automatically a bad guy. They were packed to the limit with other projects and had no room for me. It's simply awful to sit and wait while there's the prospect of an answer to Alzheimer's, even if the BSE work is never needed. We have some of the best research groups in the world here in the UK and we *must* get going.'

'So now we have found out that BSE looks like it infected humans, is unlikely to have been derived from scrapie, may well have been passed from cow to calf, and that the soil the cattle graze on will have been contaminated simply from 99.9% of the infection they eat falling out of their back end', he said. 'Lacey had said all that in 1989 amid

262

showers of abuse and denial from MAFF. So, is Lacey right about the rest?'

'What do you mean? The prediction that BSE simply won't go away? The ideas that there will be an epidemic in humans and that we will have become infected from BSE after the famous offal ban in 1989 that was supposed to render all beef safe? I'm afraid things are not looking good. At the moment, the size of the BSE epidemic in humans simply cannot be quantified but it could be very large indeed. The apparently slow fall in BSE case numbers (after apparent under-reporting is taken into account) and the calculations showing that the public health risk taken after 1989 was unacceptably high are both worrying. Hopefully the Government will not just sit and wait to see what happens.'

'Are you sure you don't need a soap box to stand on? There's still Speakers' Corner left to hear about this!'

'I hope that was a joke – come to think of it, it's good to hear a joke after all this time! No – no matter how right I might be, nobody loves the messenger who brings bad news. What I might need is a job!'

Data tables

Table 1: countries that have been affected by BSE

Oman. Two animals born in 1983 and imported into the Sultanate of Oman in 1985 as part of a consignment of 14. The animals were exposed to feedstuffs in calfhood in the UK. So BSE was in the feed in 1985 and probably in 1983. January 1990.

A case appeared in **Switzerland** November 1990. This is odd in that the cow was not imported from the UK and Switzerland only imports 2 tonnes of meal from the UK a year. November 1993.

A case appeared in **Denmark**. This was a Scottish Highland cow kept near Esbjerg and imported into the country in 1988. The rest of the herd of 13 have been destroyed. *Veterinary Record*, 22 August 1992.

Switzerland has now had 203 cases and France 13. March 1996.

Four cattle are said to have got BSE in **Germany**; all were imported from the UK in 1994.

Four further cattle with BSE have been reported in **Portugal**. One apparently occurred in the great-granddaughter of a cow imported from the UK and the others in the offspring of imported cattle. *Veterinary Record*, 10 September 1994.

I have now heard that the numbers are much higher in

Portugal and 12 cases, mostly the offspring of imports, have been found. 1995.

One case reported from the **Falkland Islands**. A cow imported from the UK. *Spongiform Encephalopathies*, Churchill Livingstone, 1993.

Italy had reported 2 cases of BSE by 1996. No reference.

The **Republic of Ireland** reported cases of BSE, thought to be due to the importation of MBM in 1989. All the herds were destroyed.

Switzerland now has over 200 cases of BSE. All of them are in internally bred cattle and one has been shown never to have been fed any MBM. 1994.

One case reported in **Canada** in 1993 in a bull imported for breeding.

Five cases had been reported in **France** by 1992. There is great disbelief among British farmers that this is the correct number.

Table 2: animals felt to have become infected with BSE

1986	Nyala (*Tragelaphus angasi*)
1987	Gemsbok (*Oryx gazella*)
8 August 1989	Greater kudu (*Tragelaphus strepisiceros*) called Linda, aged 30 months, died after only three days of clinical symptoms
21 April 1990	SE in an eland (*Taurotragus oryx*). Fleetwood and Furley
19 May 1990	SE in a five-year-old neutered Siamese cat. J.M. Wyatt, Bristol
29 September 1990	BSE transmitted to a pig by intra-cerebral inoculation. M. Dawson, CVL
24 November 1990	Ten cats with FSE had been reported. Collee, *Lancet*

14 December 1990	'First case of BSE in victim's offspring.' *The Independent*, 14 December 1990 The calf of a kudu developed BSE at London Zoo; its mother had died of it, and they did not think that it had been fed any infective food
1990	Arabian oryx (*Oryx leucoryx*)
1990	Eland (*Taurotragus oryx*)
14 September 1991	Naturally occurring scrapie-like encephalopathy in five domestic cats. *Veterinary Record*
1991	Marmoset monkey (*Callithrix jacchus*)
1991	Ostriches (*Struthio camellus*) reported from two zoos in north-west Germany. Not confirmed as a TSE yet. First case was in 1986 but two more in 1988 and 1989. Other ostriches with similar signs had died but had not been examined at post-mortem
4 March 1992	Marmoset monkey (*Callithrix jacchus*) infected with BSE by inoculation (and another by scrapie) announced in the House of Commons
1992	Cheetah (*Acinonyx jubatus*) exported from the UK to Perth in Western Australia
1992	Puma (*Felis concolor*). Willoughby, *Veterinary Record*, 1 November 1992
1992	Moufflon (*Ovis musimon*): several cases in British zoos. Wood et al., *Veterinary Record* 130, p.25
1992	Pig transmission. By 1993 between 7 and 10 pigs had been infected
1993	Sheep: between 4 and 11 by inoculation and between 3 and 12 by oral administration. The areas inside the brain that were most affected were not classic of scrapie, i.e. BSE did not cause scrapie, it caused BSE in sheep

1993	Goat transmission: three out of three by inoculation and one out of three by oral transmission
1993	100% of mice fed BSE had died and 791 inoculated it
	Cattle were fed BSE in 1991 (?) and no cases of BSE in the animal group had been reported by 1995
1993	Scimitar-horned oryx (*Oryx dammah*)
1994	Highland cat (civet)

By 1994 the numbers of zoo animals had risen

Species	number
Nyala	1
Eland	4
Arabian oryx	1
Greater kudu	> 6
Scimitar-horned oryx	1
Puma	1
Cheetah	4
Ostrich	3
Gemsbok	1
Civet	1

Because these diseases with BSE are connected in both time and geography it must be assumed that they are the same condition but in different species

Table 3: range of species to which TSE from various other species can be transmitted

	Host (donor)									
Recipient	CJD	Scrapie	TME	Kuru	BSE	CWDD	Mouse	Hamster	Goat	Rat
Human	+	NT	NT	+	NT*	NT	NT	NT	NT	NT
Sheep	-	+	+	-	+	NT	+	NT	NT	NT
Mink	-	+	+	+	+	NT	NT	NT	NT	NT
Cow	+	+	+	NT	+	NT	NT	NT	NT	NT
Deer	NT	NT	NT	NT	NT	+	NT	NT	NT	NT
Chimpanzee	+	-	-	+	NT	NT	NT	NT	-	NT
Gibbon	-	-	-	+	NT	NT	NT	NT	NT	NT
New-world monkeys										
Capuchin	+	-	NT	+	NT	NT	NT	NT	NT	NT
Marmoset	+	+	NT	+	+	NT	+	NT	NT	NT
Spider	NT	NT	NT	+	NT	NT	NT	NT	NT	NT
Squirrel	+	+	+	+	NT	NT	+	NT	+	NT
Woolly	+	NT	NT	+	NT	NT	NT	NT	NT	NT
Old-world monkeys										
African green	+	-	NT	-	NT	NT	-	NT	NT	NT
Baboon	+	NT	NT	NT	NT	NT	NT	NT	NT	NT
Bonnet	NT	NT	NT	+	NT	NT	NT	NT	NT	NT
Bush baby	+	+	NT	+	NT	NT	+	NT	NT	NT
Cynomolgus	-	NT	NT	-	NT	NT	NT	NT	NT	NT
Managabey	+	NT	NT	-	NT	NT	NT	NT	NT	NT
Patas	+	NT	NT	NT	NT	NT	NT	NT	NT	NT
Pig-tailed	+	NT	NT	+	NT	NT	NT	NT	NT	NT
Rhesus	-	-	+	+	NT	NT	-	NT	NT	NT
Stump-tailed	-	NT	+	-	NT	NT	NT	NT	NT	NT

	Talapoin	Goat	Ferret	Cat	Dog	Racoon	Skunk	Mouse	Rat	Hamster	Gerbil	Vole	Guinea pig	Rabbit	Pig	Puma	Cheetah	Kudu	Nyala	Gemsbok	Eland	Oryx	Scimitar-horned oryx	Moufflon	Civet
	+	NT	NT	NT	+	NT	NT	+	NT	NT	+	+	NT	NT	NT	NT	NT	NT	NT	NT	NT	NT	NT	NT	NT
	+	NT	NT	+	+	+	+	+	+	+	+	+	NT	NT	NT	NT	NT	NT	NT	NT	NT	NT	NT	NT	NT
	+	NT	+	+	+	+	+	+	+	+	+	−	NT	NT	NT	NT	NT	NT	NT	NT	NT	NT	NT	NT	NT
	+	−	−	−	−	−	−	−	+	−	−	−	NT	NT	NT	NT	NT	NT	NT	NT	NT	NT	NT	NT	NT
	NT	NT	NT	NT	−	−	−	−	−	−	−	−	NT	NT	NT	NT	NT	NT	NT	NT	NT	NT	NT	NT	NT
	NT	NT	NT	NT	+	+	+	NT	NT	NT	+	+	NT	NT	NT	NT	NT	NT	NT	NT	NT	NT	NT	NT	NT
	+	+	+	+	+	+	+	+	NT	+	+	+	NT	NT	NT	NT	NT	NT	NT	NT	NT	NT	NT	NT	NT
	−	+	+	+	−	−	−	+	−	+	+	+	NT	NT	NT	NT	NT	NT	NT	NT	NT	NT	NT	NT	NT
	+	+	−	+	−	−	−	+	−	+	+	+	NT	NT	NT	NT	NT	NT	NT	NT	NT	NT	NT	NT	NT
	+	−	−	+	−	−	−	+	−	NT	+	+	NT	NT	NT	NT	NT	NT	NT	NT	NT	NT	NT	NT	NT
	NT	−	−	NT	NT	NT	NT	NT	NT	NT	+	+	NT	NT	NT	NT	NT	NT	NT	NT	NT	NT	NT	NT	NT
	+	−	−	−	−	−	−	−	−	NT	+	+	NT	NT	NT	NT	NT	NT	NT	NT	NT	NT	NT	NT	NT
	NT	NT	NT	NT	NT	NT	NT	NT	NT	NT	NT	+	NT	NT	NT	NT	NT	NT	NT	NT	NT	NT	NT	NT	NT
	NT	NT	NT	NT	NT	NT	NT	NT	NT	NT	NT	+	NT	NT	NT	NT	NT	NT	NT	NT	NT	NT	NT	NT	NT
	NT	NT	NT	NT	NT	NT	NT	NT	NT	NT	NT	+	NT	NT	NT	NT	NT	NT	NT	NT	NT	NT	NT	NT	NT
	NT	NT	NT	NT	NT	NT	NT	NT	NT	NT	NT	+	NT	NT	NT	NT	NT	NT	NT	NT	NT	NT	NT	NT	NT
	NT	NT	NT	NT	NT	NT	NT	NT	NT	NT	NT	+	NT	NT	NT	NT	NT	NT	NT	NT	NT	NT	NT	NT	NT
	NT	NT	NT	NT	NT	NT	NT	NT	NT	NT	NT	+	NT	NT	NT	NT	NT	NT	NT	NT	NT	NT	NT	NT	NT
	NT	NT	NT	NT	NT	NT	NT	NT	NT	NT	NT	+	NT	NT	NT	NT	NT	NT	NT	NT	NT	NT	NT	NT	NT
	NT	NT	NT	NT	NT	NT	NT	NT	NT	NT	NT	+	NT	NT	NT	NT	NT	NT	NT	NT	NT	NT	NT	NT	NT
	NT	NT	NT	NT	NT	NT	NT	NT	NT	NT	NT	+	NT	NT	NT	NT	NT	NT	NT	NT	NT	NT	NT	NT	NT
	NT	NT	NT	NT	NT	NT	NT	NT	NT	NT	NT	+	NT	NT	NT	NT	NT	NT	NT	NT	NT	NT	NT	NT	NT
	NT	NT	NT	NT	NT	NT	NT	NT	NT	NT	NT	+	NT	NT	NT	NT	NT	NT	NT	NT	NT	NT	NT	NT	NT
	NT	NT	NT	NT	NT	NT	NT	NT	NT	NT	NT	+	NT	NT	NT	NT	NT	NT	NT	NT	NT	NT	NT	NT	NT
	NT	NT	NT	NT	NT	NT	NT	NT	NT	NT	NT	+	NT	NT	NT	NT	NT	NT	NT	NT	NT	NT	NT	NT	NT

This is to show that some animals (along the top) with TSE can be used to infect other animals (on the left side). About 70% of the tests are successful.

+ = donor infected recipient
− = donor did not infect recipient
NT = experiment not tried
* = now considered to be +

269

Table 4: oral transmission of spongiform encephalopathy

	Donor						
Recipient	Mouse	Hamster	Sheep	Goat	Cow	Human	Mink
Mouse	85	NT	0–100	NT	100	NT	NT
Hamster	NT	100	NT	NT	NT	NT	NT
Sheep	NT	NT	15–45	NT	25	NT	NT
Goat	NT	NT	25	100	33	NT	100
Cow	NT	NT	+	NT	>17	NT	NT
Mink	NT	NT	NT	NT	+	NT	+
Monkey	NT	NT	100	NT	NT	100	+

Figures indicate percentage success of transfer of TSE from donor to recipient by an oral route, i.e. they show what percentage of the animals fed the infective tissue died of disease.

+ = success recorded but percentage not available
NT = not tested
> = more than

Table 5: number of cases of BSE according to year of birth

Year of birth	Age of bovine at the time									
	1	2	3	4	5	6	7	8	9	10
1981								43	31	19
1982							171	94	79	22
1983						887	526	230	174	
1984					2481	1853	887	539		
1985				2728	4010	2417	1070			
1986			770	5440	6288	3468				
1987		35	2130	10870	10211					
1988	1	73	4199	17859						

Figures derived from MAFF data for cases reported in each year at different ages. The cases for which the age is not known are presumed to have the same age distribution as the ones for which this distribution is known.

Some of the cattle calculated to have been born in a particular year may in fact have been born in the previous year. This is of no significance in terms of statistical calculation.

Table 6: how the missing figures from Table 5 are calculated vertically

Year of birth	Age of death	
	6	7
1984	?	3
1985	2	6
1986	3	9
1987	9	28
1988	15	47

This is an imaginary group of BSE cases where it might be possible to work out the numbers expected in the box containing the question mark. Clearly the relationship between the numbers born in different years is always the same, so you would expect one to die aged six and born in 1984.

Table 7: how the missing figures from Table 5 are calculated horizontally

Year of birth	Age of death from BSE				
	2	3	4	5	6
1986	?	4	6	8	10
1987	4	8	12	16	20
1988	8	16	24	32	?

This is an imaginary group of BSE cases where it might be possible to work out the numbers expected in the boxes containing question marks. Clearly the relationship between the numbers that die at different ages is always the same, so you would expect 40 cases to die aged six and born in 1988, and two to die aged two and born in 1986.

Table 8: ages of cattle in the UK, 1988

Age in years	Number
<1	3,367,500
1–2	2,615,750
2–3	1,420,500
3–4	1,285,000
4–5	975,000
5–6	709,000
6–7	531,000
7–8	354,000
8–9	265,000
9–10	133,000
10–11	88,500
>11	88,500

Data for milking cattle are derived from the Milk Marketing Board National Milk Records Census 1988 and are divided into numbers of cattle in each lactation. The first lactation is taken to be at approximately three years of age. Cattle which are not in milk but pregnant are taken to have a similar age distribution as those which are lactating.

Data for the number and age of young cattle and cattle in beef herds for slaughter are taken as averages from the Meat and Livestock Commission December and June Census reports 1986–92. Cows and heifers in milk from beef herds are taken to have a similar age distribution as those from milking herds. The age distribution of bulls for service is unclear, but they represent less than 1% of the bovine population.

< = less than
> = more than

273

Table 9: infectivity per gram of specific tissues in animals infected with transmissible spongiform encephalopathy

Tissue	Host				
	Sheep	Mouse	Hamster	Goat	Mink
Muscle	< 2.5	NT	+	> 1	4.0
Brain	5.2–7.4	8.9–9.3	7.5–12.1	4.0–7.3	6.0–9.5
Spinal cord	4.2–7.0	6.8–8.9	NT	NT	5.0–7.0
Nerve	2.1–4.0	5.5–6.7	NT	> 1	> 4.5
Pituitary	2.5–3.3	NT	NT	2.2	NT
Adrenal	2.2–4.0	NT	NT	2.2	NT
Spleen	5.5	5.3–7.3	5.3–6.3	2.6–3.8	4.5–6.5
Lymphoid tissue	3.2–4.9	5.6–7.0	NT	3.3–5.7	4.5
Liver	NT	> 2.5	NT	2.2	2.5–6.5
Kidney	< 2.5	> 2.5	NT	NT	2.5–6.0
Gut	5.1–5.3	7.0–7.7	NT	3.3–4.3	3.0
Salivary gland	< 2.5	NT	NT	2.3	2.5–3.5
Pancreas	< 2.5	NT	NT	> 1	NT
Thymus	NT	7.0–8.1	NT	2.2	> 2.5
Lung	< 2.5	4.7–8.3	NT	NT	4.5
Bladder	NT	NT	NT	NT	6.0
Reproductive organs	> 2	NT	NT	NT	NT

No infectivity was found in thyroid, milk or saliva. Urine was found positive in one experiment but negative in all others. Faeces was found positive in one experiment. Figures are from inoculation of multiple dilutions of tissue into an animal of the same species, except for experiments on sheep and goats which were performed on mice. These figures would be expected to be lower than the real level of infectivity.

The figures in this table are logarithms to the base 10 (i.e. $2 = 100$, $4 = 10,000$, $7 = 10,000,000$) of the number of infective units per gram of tissue. For a figure that is not a whole number, see it as being between the figure above and the one below.

Due to inadequate information being available for the methods used to measure infectivity in mice, it was assumed that the smallest amount that could be measured was 2.5 (i.e. between 2 and 3, meaning between 100 IU per gram and 1000 IU per gram). This is an underestimate.

Infectivity was found in some species in every tissue tested, but in sheep, which were tested by inoculation into mice, not all tissues were positive. Beef tissue was only positive in the brain and spinal cord, and this result has been criticised as being exceedingly unlikely for such a disease.

NT = not tested
+ = infectivity found but no experimental details
< = less than
> = more than

Table 10: products from 1000kg of choice fattened bovine

Slaughter products (kg)

Carcass			610.0
Hide			75.0
	Fat	53.5	
	Tongue	5.0	
	Liver	12.0	
	Sweetbreads	0.3	
	Tail	1.5	
	Kidneys	1.5	
	Tripe	18.0	
	Trimmings	5.2	
	Brain	0.6	
	Heart	2.7	
Offal (edible)		100.8	100.8
	Viscera	75.2	
	Blood	35.0	
	Fill	59.0	
	Head/feet	40.0	
Offal (inedible)		209.2	209.2
Other			5.0

This table shows how much we get from our beef animals and the weight of the various tissues, some of which were banned in late 1989 as Specified Bovine Offal and some of which were not.

These details were taken from a textbook published in the USA, where things are clearly sent to rendering which are used to create food here in the UK. The head, for instance, carries a lot of meat and this can be removed.

Table 11: weight and IU of various parts of 1000kg choice fattened bovine

Slaughter products		Weight (kg)	Total IU when animal has clinical symptoms
Carcass	Meat	540.0	$10^{6.7}$–$10^{7.7}$
	Bones	54.0	?
	Nerve	16.0	$10^{6.5}$–$10^{9.9}$
Hide		75.0	
Edible offal	Fat	53.5	?
	Tongue	5.0	?
	Liver	12.0	$10^{6.5}$–$10^{10.5}$
	Sweetbreads	0.3	?
	Tail	1.5	?
	Kidneys	1.5	$10^{5.7}$–$10^{9.6}$
	Tripe	18.0	?
	Trimmings	5.2	?
	Brain	0.6	$10^{10.2}$–$10^{13.2}$
	Heart	2.7	?
Inedible offal	Viscera (*gut, thymus, lungs*)	75.2	approx $10^{\dagger 1.8}$
	Blood	35	?
	Fill	59	?
	Head/Feet	40	?
Other	Including *lymphoid tissue*	5	?

Tissues banned as Specified Bovine Offal are in italics. IU levels are calculated from infectivity levels in Table 9.

This table shows just how much infectivity is expected to exist in the tissues of a cow with symptoms of BSE. The figures are logarithmic (for explanation, see note at foot of Table 9).

Under inedible offal there are parts that we do actually eat – lungs, for instance – which have been shown in some experiments to be highly infective in mice.

When it came to calculating the amount of infectivity in the tissues it was almost impossible with the majority of them. Not enough data was available either on the amount of a particular tissue present, or on how infective it was likely to be. As a result, large amounts of what we eat could not be adequately estimated in terms of BSE risk. This applies to bone marrow, for instance, which is used in large amounts and is very likely to be infective because of the immune tissue present. As a result it was decided to calculate risks purely on the human diet of meat, peripheral nerve (as 10% of the total amount in the cow), liver and kidney. Clearly these are underestimates and the total infectivity from an individual animal should be assumed to be much greater.

Table 12: brain TSE infectivity of different species at different percentages of the incubation period

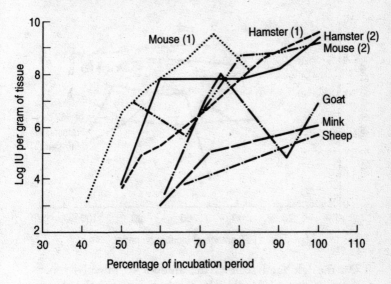

On the left-hand scale is the amount of infectivity per gram, as measured in IU. The numbers represent the power of 10 involved (see note at foot of Table 9). At the top of the scale it is 10,000,000,000 IU per gram (i.e. 1 gram of the brain is enough to infect ten thousand million other animals of the same species)! It is not surprising that doctors are worried about the risks from CJD cadaver brains, as 1 gram from them could be enough to poison the entire human population.

It can be seen that the infectivity rises from about 40% of the incubation period and generally goes up and up until the animal dies.

Table 13: spleen TSE infectivity of different species at different percentages of the incubation period

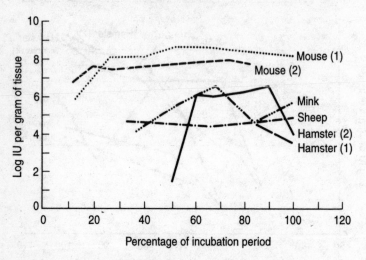

On the left-hand scale is the amount of infectivity per gram, as measured in IU. The numbers represent the power of 10 involved (see note at foot of Table 9). At the top of the scale it is 10,000,000,000 IU per gram (i.e. 1 gram of the brain is enough to infect ten thousand million other animals of the same species)! The infectivity of the spleen does not quite reach such high levels as the brain.

You can see how the infectivity rises from early in the incubation period and rises to a steady level. This effect would be expected with a number of parts of the body that contain a lot of immune tissue, e.g. the liver. It is probably due to the slow turnover of the immune cells (i.e. they are gradually being replaced) that the IU levels don't rise so high as in brain. All the time new, presumably uninfected cells are being produced and old, infected ones are dying. In the brain, however, the lack of any turnover means that the infection just keeps on building up until the cells are killed.

Table 14: UK population intake of beef and beef products

Relative intake	male			female		
	beef	liver/ kidney/ heart	beef sausage	beef	liver/ kidney/ heart	beef sausage
0	2.4	48.6	32.3	4.6	49.1	47.1
0.5	3.6	27.6	19.8	5.3	27.2	19.0
1	12.0	19.7	26.9	15.9	20.1	22.9
2	22.8	3.1	11.8	23.3	2.5	7.4
3	26.1	0.7	4.4	25.0	0.8	2.2
4	16.7	0.3	1.3	13.0	0.2	0.7
5	8.4	0	0.8	7.4	0.1	0.2
6	3.2	0	0.2	2.0	0	0
7	4.7	0.1	0.4	3.4	0.1	0.4

Data derived from the Scottish Heart Health Study, collected 1984–6 in people aged 40–59. Beefburgers are taken to have a similar distribution to sausages.

The figures in the far left-hand column are the relative amount eaten by a particular person. The figure 1 means a standard amount of food. For instance, from column 2 you can see that 12% of men eat this standard amount, whereas 4.7% of men eat seven times this amount.

What the table particularly shows is that some foods (e.g. beef) are eaten by almost everyone, but some (e.g. liver) are eaten by a smaller number and in smaller amounts.

When I calculated the number of people that would have eaten different amounts of infectivity I had to use this table to calculate the weight of food they ate.

Table 15: numbers of people (millions) in the UK who would be expected to have eaten more than the indicated potential infective doses of BSE by 1997

Potential infective dose (IU)	Relative infectivity of beef in diet		
	High	Medium	Low
10^3	34.44	34.44	34.44
10^4	34.44	34.44	34.43
			(34.03)
10^5	34.43	32.71	5.66
	(34.35)	(30.51)	(2.76)
10^6	34.16	8.23	0
	(33.57)	(8.17)	
10^7	19.08	0	0
	(17.75)		
10^8	8.23	0	0
	(1.35)		
10^9	0	0	0

Figures in brackets were calculated assuming that beef suckler herd cows had minimal risk of BSE and that cattle developing BSE over the age of six years had an incubation period mean of five years.

These figures relate only to the 34,656,622 people between the ages of 16 and 59 years. Adequate data for the beef intake of younger or older groups is not available.

If the calculated BSE incidence is varied by 25% little change is seen in the figures in this table. The reason for this is that the scale for the amount of infectivity needed to infect a human is logarithmic (see note at foot of Table 9).

The data seen here assumes that humans have only eaten liver, kidney, muscle and 10% of peripheral nerves. It assumes that no other tissues have ever been eaten, that all cattle with symptoms are reported, that all the cases of BSE are identified by microscopy of the brain. In other words, the figures here are as if MAFF data is perfect.

Clearly we have eaten many other tissues, both before and after the specified offals ban in November 1989; some cattle will have not been reported, and some cases will not be identified. The results here should therefore be assumed to be underestimates.

Table 16: cumulative BSE case numbers that were born in specific months after June 1988

Year of report	Month of birth 1988						1989									total
	Jul*	Aug	Sep	Oct	Nov	Dec	Jan	Feb	Mar	Apr	May	Jun	Jul	Aug	Sep	
1992	234	782	913	525	269	170	96	60	45	30	30	51	57	60	63	3385
1993	259	1249	1531	964	505	296	180	106	91	70	41	83	167	256	234	6032

*The collection of data started approximately halfway through July 1988
The figures represent BSE cattle reported by the end of the reporting year, and include all those reported in previous years

This table shows that in 1992 and 1993 various numbers of cattle born after the feed ban (BABs) developed BSE.

Because we can work out the age at which the cattle died, we can predict the number that would be expected to die from the same month group the following year. The numbers that actually appeared were very much too low, giving a reporting rate of under 30% for BSE in BABs in 1993. Although this is not exactly the same as calculated by the other statistical method, it is sufficiently similar to indicate that large numbers of cases are not reaching MAFF records.

Table 17: age of cattle reported with BSE in the UK 1989–93

Year of birth	Age of animal with BSE								
	2	3	4	5	6	7	8	9	10
79–80	NA	NA	NA	NA	NA	NA	NA	17[1]	18[2]
80–81	NA	NA	NA	NA	NA	NA	62[1]	43[2]	40[3]
81–82	NA	NA	NA	NA	NA	198[1]	123[2]	83[3]	50[4]
82–83	NA	NA	NA	NA	879[1]	521[2]	225[3]	172[4]	83[5]
83–84	NA	NA	NA	2275[1]	1918[2]	950[3]	440[4]	244[5]	NA
84–85	NA	NA	2557[1]	4065[2]	2561[3]	1268[4]	632[5]	NA	NA
85–86	NA	781[1]	4399[2]	5741[3]	4073[4]	1983[5]	NA	NA	NA
86–87	49[1]	1744[2]	8847[3]	10907[4]	7865[5]	NA	NA	NA	NA
87–88	73[2a]	4227[3b]	16039[4c]	17637[5]	NA	NA	NA	NA	NA
88–89	85[3d]	2015[4e]	7497[5]	NA	NA	NA	NA	NA	NA
89–90	40[4f]	1208[5]	NA	NA	NA	NA	NA	NA	NA
90–91	23[5]	NA	NA	NA	NA	NA	NA	NA	NA

NA = not available

Data assumes that reported BSE cases of unknown age have the same age distribution as those in which this age is known.

[1-5] = numbers of BSE cases that were reported in specific years, 1989 to 1993 respectively.

[a-f] = numbers of cases that may have been born after the feed ban and which were found to be statistically too low to fit in with numbers either above or to the left of them.

Data from 1994 and 1995 are now difficult to validate but available from MAFF.

Note that cattle born in 1987–8 may well have been fed infective material before the feed ban but for only a short period. Cattle born in previous years would be expected to have been exposed to progressively longer periods in which infectivity might have been in their feed. The fact that the alterations in this period seems to have made no difference in the age distribution of cases of BSE is one of the factors that suggests that infection takes place at a single point – in which case there should be no change in this age distribution after the feed ban, and all that should have altered was the overall number of cases.

Table 18: proportion of cattle dying of BSE at different ages

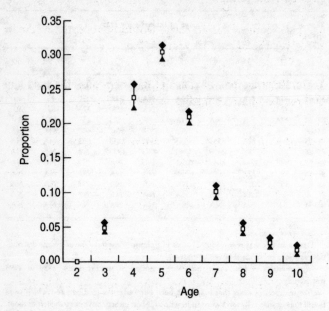

The figures on the left-hand side (the y axis) represent the part of the total number of cattle (born in the same year)* that would die at the age shown on the bottom scale (x axis). For instance, 0.25 (or 25%) of the cattle born in 1985 would die of BSE aged four, and about 0.3 (or 30%) would die aged five.

On the graph there are little bars above and below a middle square. From the top to the bottom of these two bars is what is called the 95% confidence interval, i.e. there is a 95% certainty that the true value will be between the top of the top bar and the bottom of the lower bar.

This graph is known as the age distribution of cases and is particularly important in that it shows that before the feed ban in 1988 the age distribution stays closely the same throughout the epidemic. This is strange if BSE was derived from scrapie.

*this assumes that no cattle would be reported to die of BSE over the age of 10 years.

Table 19: proportion of cases of BSE born after the feed ban that reached MAFF statistics in 1992 and 1993

| Year of birth | Reporting year | | | | | |
| | 1992 | | | | 1993 | |
	estimate	95% CI upper	lower	estimate	95% CI upper	lower
1987–8	0.78	0.70	0.87	0.66	0.58	0.74
after 1987–8	0.53	0.32	0.87	0.39	0.24	0.65

CI = confidence interval (see note at foot of Table 18)

As can be seen, the percentage seems to have dropped from what was taken as 100% reporting in 1991 to 39% in 1993. The proportion in 1994 may well be even lower as the amount of compensation for farmers dropped at the beginning of that year.

Table 20: number of cases of clinical BSE that would have been reported in UK in separate years

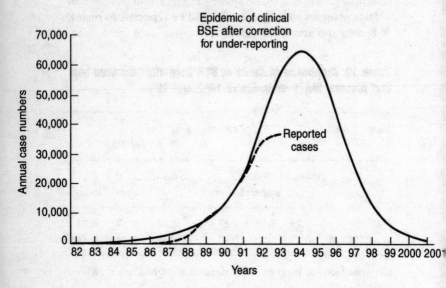

This graph shows that the number of cases, after correction for under-reporting, would have been much greater than those reported in the years prior to 1989, in 1992 and in 1993. These figures are calculated with assumptions that no cattle born after 1991 ever develop BSE, and this is what gives rise to the drop in the number of cases leading up to the year 2000. If the vertical transmission hypothesis is assumed to be correct, it is possible to calculate the number of cases that would be expected in these years. Again a fall is seen, but this time to between 10,000 and 20,000 cases in 2000. If Professor Lacey turns out to be correct and the disease becomes 'endemic', i.e. current cases causing further cases, we may not see any drop at all.

Remember that the case numbers depend on the farmer recognising BSE in a cow, him reporting it to the veterinary officer, the VO agreeing and buying the cow, the animal being slaughtered and the sample of brain being good enough for diagnosis to be made. In other words, all reported figures are expected to be underestimates but we have no better measure of the true numbers at this time.

Table 21: number of cattle dying of BSE altogether by the age of 10 years and born in different years

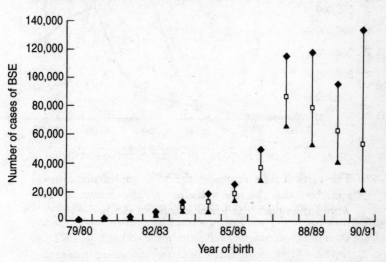

After taking into account the under-reporting that appears to have taken place after the feed ban, the number of cases of BSE (on the left scale, y axis) that would be seen in the groups of cattle born in different years (on the lower scale, x axis) can be recalculated. It can be seen that the results are not specific numbers but bars. All we can say is that we are 95% certain that the true result is somewhere between the top of the bar and the bottom. The point of the small square in the line is where the true value is most likely to be.

Table 22: number of infected cattle born in specific years that would be eaten by humans before showing symptoms of BSE

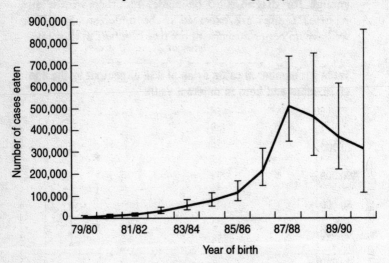

The vertical bars represent the 95% confidence interval and show that the true value has a 95% chance of being within the upper and lower margin of the bar.

Table 23: calculated numbers of cases of BSE in cattle born in specific years if not slaughtered for food

Year of birth	Cases of BSE that would develop between 2 and 10 yrs	
	Estimate	95% confidence interval
1979–80	4655	2170–9993
1980–1	9488	5701–15788
1981–2	14458	9580–21808
1982–3	28927	20274–41249
1983–4	51901	37513–71749
1984–5	73273	54028–99274
1985–6	107575	80413–143724
1986–7	204703	154544–270479
1987–8	466758	359528–602811

Figures are corrected for under-reporting rates in 1989, 1992 and 1993 and for the low rate of BSE in beef herds.

Table 24: numbers of cattle that would be expected to die of BSE in UK without slaughter for human food

| Year of birth | Bovine numbers | |
	estimate	95% confidence interval
1979–80	4756	2006–11191
1980–1	9700	5273–17695
1981–2	14792	8864–24463
1982–3	29654	18787–46395
1983–4	53376	34844–81044
1984–5	75582	50301–112571
1985–6	111503	75142–164007
1986–7	215157	145943–314402
1987–8	510405	349955–737891
1988–9	464060	283193–753770
1989–90	369736	220352–614934
1990–1	315637	114882–859586

Table 25: percentage of bovine offspring in UK herds expected to develop BSE without slaughter for human food

| Year of birth | Bovine numbers | |
	estimate	95% confidence interval
1979–80	0.14	0.06–0.33
1980–1	0.29	0.16–0.53
1981–2	0.44	0.26–0.73
1982–3	0.88	0.56–1.38
1983–4	1.59	1.03–2.41
1984–5	2.24	1.49–3.34
1985–6	3.31	2.23–4.87
1986–7	6.39	4.33–9.34
1987–8	15.16	10.39–21.91
1988–9	13.78	8.41–22.38
1989–90	10.98	6.54–18.26
1990–1	9.37	3.41–25.53

Table 26: percentage of bovine offspring in UK herds expected to develop BSE without slaughter for human food and assuming that all cases are the offspring of dairy herds that make up 60% of the UK herd

Year of birth	Bovine numbers estimate	95% confidence interval
1979–80	0.24	0.10–0.55
1980–1	0.48	0.26–0.88
1981–2	0.73	0.44–1.21
1982–3	1.47	0.93–2.30
1983–4	2.64	1.72–4.01
1984–5	3.74	2.49–5.57
1985–6	5.52	3.72–8.12
1986–7	10.65	7.22–15.56
1987–8	25.26	17.32–36.52
1988–9	22.97	14.02–37.31
1989–90	18.30	10.91–30.43
1990–1	15.62	5.69–42.54

Table 27: number of cattle eaten in specific years that were incubating BSE at the time of slaughter

	Bovine numbers	
Year of slaughter	estimate	95% confidence interval
1980	1007	419–2395
1981	3720	1795–7753
1982	6720	3753–11956
1983	12270	7373–20317
1984	23459	14717–37119
1985	38003	24476–58463
1986	56264	36887–84968
1987	95097	63126–141740
1988	199593	134035–293993
1989	303227	197278–462223
1990	291791	177797–474410
1991	280629	155207–529483
1992	211238	102667–463857
1993	99623	57097–176669
1994	82249	41913–167552
1995	49488	23399–107397
1996	26630	12220–58510
1997	14253	5844–34460
1998	5900	2378–14235
1999	2935	923–8769
2000	415	110–1382
Totals:	1804512	1063414–3157650

As can be seen, the peak seems to have taken place in 1989 but this gives a misleading idea of when the most infectivity would be eaten. This is because cattle are generally eaten between one and three years old and are not very infective compared with those eaten at a later part of their incubation period. As a result the peak in the amount of infectivity being eaten is likely to be 1993–4.

Remember that these numbers assume that no cattle born after 1991 ever develop BSE. Currently we are not even sure that BSE is dropping at all, but if it is falling as the number of infected bovine mothers drops then we will expect the infectivity in human food to fall too. Clearly the numbers after 1992 are underestimates.

Table 28: number of cattle born in specific years that would later develop BSE

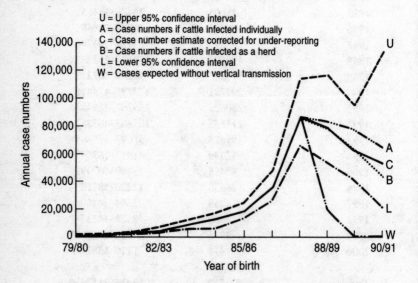

It is now clear that the number of cases is not dropping rapidly after the ban, as would have been expected if BSE was purely transmitted by the feed.

Could BSE be transmitted from the mother? The number of cases expected is shown (line A) if a relatively small percentage of the mothers are infected but all their off-

296

spring catch it from them. The number of cases expected is shown (line B) if all the mothers became infected and a relatively low percentage of their offspring become infected. What we are finding is estimated by line C, and this is very similar to B.

The current problem is that we are unsure exactly how many cases are appearing. This means that we cannot be sure which of the possible causes of BSE cases born after the feed ban are correct. However, infectivity remaining in the feed seems extremely unlikely as the cause.

Table 29: adult population numbers (millions) in the UK that would be expected to have eaten a potentially fatal dose of BSE by 2001

Infective dose (IU)	Relative infectivity of bovine tissues with respect to TSEs in other species		
	High	Medium	Low
10^3	33.75* (33.75–33.75)**	33.75 (33.75–33.75)	33.75 (33.75–33.75)
10^4	33.75 (33.75–33.75)	33.75 (25.5–33.75)	20.47 (11.44–28.35)
10^5	33.75 (33.75–33.75)	20.47 (18.98–20.47)	0.38 (0.29–1.35)
10^6	32.5 (22.2–33.75)	17.82 (17.82–17.82)	0
10^7	17.82 (17.82–23.4)	0.38 (0.034–1.35)	0
10^8	17.82 (8.28–17.82)	0	0
10^9	0.14 (0.034–1.35)	0	0

*Statistics are only available for the diet of adults in the UK aged between 16 and 59 (34.66 million).

**Figures in brackets represent the upper and lower 95% confidence intervals. Figures are often the same due to the effects of logarithmic groupings.

Table 30: UK meals (millions), containing enough infectivity in 100g of bovine tissue to individually represent a human risk, and eaten by the human population by 1999

BSE infectivity contained in meal (IU)	Relative infectivity of dietary beef tissue		
	Low	Medium	High
10^3	195 (155–240)	195 (154–241)	219 (174–270)
10^4	6.6 (5.4–8.1)	134 (106–165)	197 (156–242)
10^5	0	8.3 (6.8–10.1)	197 (156–242)
10^6	0	0 (6.1–9.2)	9.7 (8.6–11.6)
10^7	0	0	7.9 (6.3–9.6)
10^8	0	0	5.7 (4.5–7.0)

The figures represent the number of human meals that will contain more IU than needed to kill a person by mouth. The left-hand scale (y axis) is the possible amount of IU needed to do this. The three columns of figures depend on whether BSE-infected tissue turns out to be highly infective (on the right), not very infective (on the left) or between the two (in the middle). At the moment we have no good knowledge which of these is correct.

Figures in brackets represent the upper and lower limits of the 95% confidence intervals. In other words there is a 95% chance that the true figure is between the two figures. The numbers are calculated from the number of infected cattle eaten by 1999 by the human population before showing signs of disease. It assumes that humans have never eaten any of the specified offals such as brain, and that no cattle born after 1991 will ever show signs of disease. The numbers are therefore very much an underestimate.

Only 50% of bovine tissue meals are assumed to be of tissue from a single animal. Meals of muscular tissue are assumed to contain 0.2% by weight of peripheral nerve (i.e. that 10% of peripheral nerve reaches the human diet in this form). Meal numbers are calculated assuming that each contains 100g of tissue.

Clearly we don't know which of the columns is the right one and we don't know how many IU are needed to infect us. As a result we must assume that any of the results could be correct and hence, as 12 of the 18 numbers are in millions, there may be a 12 out of 18 chance that millions of people would eat potentially fatal doses of BSE in a single meal by 1999.

Table 31: chance of first BSE infection taking place in specific years

Year of first infection	Percentage of herds becoming infected for the first time in this year
1987	0.67
1988	4.23
1989	7.31
1990	10.55
1991	12.71
1992	14.56
1993 (estimate)	18.00

Data derived from the epidemic curve of home-bred cases of BSE. The 1993 estimate is derived from MAFF data for infected herds as a percentage of total UK herds.

Table 32: months in which cattle that are going to die of BSE are born

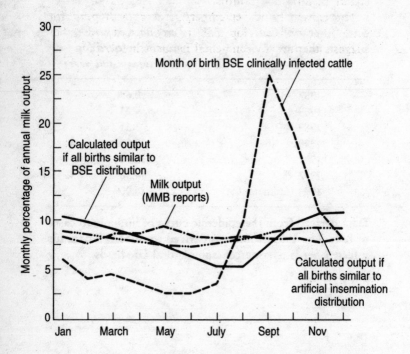

As can be seen, there is a huge peak in September and October. If this was true for all the cattle there would be a huge peak in milk production just afterwards and a shortage of it in June, July and August the following year.

'Autumn calving' was the normal practice for cattle and there was a minor 'spring calving' also. The Milk Marketing Board (MMB) did not want such peaks and troughs of milk production, however, as the demand for milk was fairly static throughout the year. As a result they decided to pay more for milk in the summer than at other times and as a result cattle now calve throughout the year. This is made clear by the months at which artificial insemination takes place being now fairly steady in different months.

The cause of the September/October birth peak for cattle that will develop BSE is as yet unknown, but suggests that an environmental factor is involved.

Glossary of abbreviations and technical terms

ADAS Agriculture Development and Advisory Service, administered by MAFF.

AFRC The Agriculture and Food Research Council. The group that decides where funding should go for research.

Asymptomatic Showing no symptoms, but possibly this is true during the incubation period of the disease.

Autoclaving Heating up under pressure to kill live organisms. To kills TSEs requires 135 degrees Centigrade for 15 minutes.

BAB Born after the Ban. This is the term used for cattle born after the 1988 ban on the presence of bovine tissue in cattle feed that nevertheless went on to develop BSE.

BMA British Medical Association.

CJD Creutzfeldt-Jakob disease.

Clinically sick Showing signs and symptoms of disease.

CPHL Central Public Health Laboratory at Colindale in north London, administered by the Department of Health.

CWDD Chronic wasting disease of deer (a TSE).

CVL Central Veterinary Laboratory at Weybridge.

DoH Department of Health in the UK Government.

EC European Community (later the European Union or EU and earlier the European Economic Community or EEC, but for convenience EC is used in most contexts in this book.

Fraction   A part of a sample after separation.

FSE   Feline spongiform encephalopathy.

GSS   Gerstmann-Straussler-Scheinker syndrome. An inherited condition in which a proportion of the people holding a specific gene develop a TSE.

Histology   The study of tissues under the microscope.

Horizontal transmission   The passage of a disease from one animal to another through various forms of contact (touch, air etc.).

Inoculum   The amount put into the body of a recipient, e.g. inoculation by mouth (usually a tablet, or via a tube into the stomach).

i.p.   Infectious particle or intra-peritoneal.

i.c.   Intra-cerebral (i.e. inoculated into the brain).

IU   Infective unit. This is the smallest amount of infectivity that is able to transmit a TSE from one animal to another of the same species.

Kuru   A human TSE found in the Fore tribe of New Guinea as a result of ritualistic cannibalistic practices that allowed people with brain disease to be eaten.

MAFF   Ministry of Agriculture, Fisheries and Food in the UK Government.

MLC   Meat and Livestock Commission.

MBM   Meat and bone meal. Used to describe the powdered remains of the animal that is often used as either fertiliser or feed for other animals.

MRM   Mechanically recovered meat.

NFU   National Farmers' Union.

Pathogenesis   The progression of disease by the damage to tissues, and the mechanism by which this takes place.

Prion   A protein infectious agent (often written as PrP^{res} or PrP^{sc}).

Prion protein   A normal protein produced by nervous tissue and some others, whose action is unknown. This is the protein that is thought to be converted into the prion (it is often written as PrP^c).

Ruminants Groups of animals that digest in a specific way, e.g. sheep, goats, deer, cattle.

SAF Scrapie associated fibrils, specific crystalloid fragments that are seen under the electron microscope when looking at extracts of brain infected with a TSE.

Scrapie A TSE of sheep and goats that appears to be transmissible to other species. The reason for the condition is not known and an association with the land on which the animals live seems to be involved.

SEAC Spongiform Encephalopathy Advisory Committee, a committee set up by MAFF and the DoH to advise on the action that should be taken concerning BSE.

SBO Specified bovine offals.

SOB Specified Offals Ban. This was the ban that came into force in November 1989 to prevent certain tissues from cattle from being present in human food.

Species barrier The apparent difficulty encountered when trying to pass a TSE from one species to another. A high dose is required and a long incubation period results.

SE Spongiform encephalopathy.

TME Transmissible mink encephalopathy.

Transgenic The passing of a gene from one animal to another using complex genetic techniques. A resulting mouse, for instance, would be known as a transgenic mouse.

TSE Transmissible spongiform encephalopathy.

USDA United States Department of Agriculture.

Vertical transmission The passage of a disease from parent to offspring.

Virino A possible form of the infectious agent of TSEs in which a small piece of DNA or RNA is wrapped up in a protein.

VO Veterinary officer hired by MAFF.